W9-CHO-631

Reading Room

The Way of the World

The Way of the World

Eldonna L. Evertts / Language Arts
Lyman C. Hunt / Reading
Bernard J. Weiss / Linguistics and Curriculum

Edited by Jane Berkowitz and Craig Bettinger
Educational Consultants: Patsy Montague and Janet Sprout

THE HOLT BASIC READING SYSTEM
• LEVEL 10 •

HOLT, RINEHART AND WINSTON, INC.
New York / Toronto / London / Sydney

Copyright © 1973 by Holt, Rinehart and Winston, Inc.
All Rights Reserved
Printed in the United States of America
ISBN: 0-03-080073-0
6789   071   9876

Illustrated by

Victor Valla, pages 14-21

Miriam Schottland, pages 22-33

Museum of the City of New York, page 34

Diane de Groat, pages 35, 39 (top and bottom left), 40 (top, middle right, bottom), 41 (top right) 96-101, 169, 246-255, 286-287

MAGNUM: Rene Burri, page 38 (bottom); Ernst Haas, page 39 (bottom right); Bruce Davidson, page 40 (middle left); Charles Harbutt, page 41 (top left)

Ingbet, photos, pages 42-43, 190-191, 256-257

Muriel Wood, pages 44-58, 192-202

Tad Krumeich, pages 59, 92, 125, 147, 203, 219

Bernie D'Andrea, pages 60-75

Bernice Myers, pages 76-91

NASA, photo, page 93

George Senty, pages 102, 109

Holden Weintraub, page 103

Bob Goldstein, pages 104-108

Symeon Shimin, pages 110-123

Tim and Greg Hildebrandt, pages 124, 172-189

Tom Upshur, pages 126-138

Marie Michal, page 139

Charles Lily, pages 140-146

Denver Gillen, pages 148-160

Norman Green, pages 204-217

Leslie Bauman, photo, page 218

Colos, pages 221-227

Elizabeth Levy, photos, pages 228-230, 233-235

National Oceanic and Atmospheric Administration, photo, page 231

Kyuzo Tsugami, pages 236-245

Jerry Pinkney, pages 258-285

Cover, pages 6-13, 94-95, and 170-171 constructed by S. N. Studio.

Acknowledgments

Grateful acknowledgment is given to the following authors and publishers:

Addison-Wesley Publishing Company, Inc., for "The Flying Patchwork Quilt," adapted from *The Flying Patchwork Quilt,* a Young Scott Book by Barbara Brenner. Copyright © 1965 by Barbara Brenner. Used by permission.

Atheneum Publishers, Inc., for "Until I Saw the Sea," from *I Feel the Same Way* by Lilian Moore. Copyright © 1967 by Lilian Moore. Used by permission.

Coward, McCann & Geoghegan, Inc., for "Oasis of the Stars," adapted from *Oasis of the Stars* by Olga Economakis. Copyright © 1965 by Olga Economakis. Used by permission.

Follett Publishing Company, for "The Collector," from *That Was Summer* by Marci Ridlon. Copyright © 1969 by Marci Ridlon. Used by permission.

Grosset & Dunlap, for "I Can Fly," from *At the Top of My Voice and Other Poems* by Felice Holman. Copyright © 1970 by Felice Holman. Used by permission.

Harvey House, Inc., for "The Sunflower Garden," adapted from *The Sunflower Garden* by Janice May Udry. Copyright © 1969 by Harvey House, Inc. Used by permission of the Evelyn Singer Agency.

Little, Brown and Company, and Andre Deutsch, Ltd., for "Walker, the Witch, and the Striped Flying Saucer," adapted from *Walker, the Witch, and the Striped Flying Saucer* by James Stevenson. Copyright © 1969 by James Stevenson. Used by permission.

The Macmillan Company, for "February Twilight," from *Collected Poems of Sara Teasdale,* copyright 1926 by The Macmillan Company, renewed 1954 by Mamie T. Wheless; "The Beaver," from *Toucans Two and Other Poems* by Jack Prelutsky, copyright © 1967 by Jack Prelutsky. Used by permission.

McGraw-Hill Book Company, for "Valentine for Earth," from *The Little Whistler* by Frances Frost. Copyright 1949 by McGraw-Hill, Inc. Used by permission.

Thomas Nelson & Sons, for "In the Country," from *That's Why* by Aileen Fisher, copyright 1946. Used by permission.

Parents' Magazine Press, for "Why the Sun Was Late," adapted from *Why the Sun Was Late* by Benjamin Elkin, copyright © 1966 by Benjamin Elkin; for "Such Is the Way of the World," adapted from *Such Is the Way of the World* by Benjamin Elkin, copyright © 1968 by Benjamin Elkin; for "Butch Elects a Mayor," adapted from *Butch Elects a Mayor* by Helene Hanff, copyright © 1969 by Helene Hanff. Used by permission.

Prentice-Hall, Inc., and McIntosh and Otis, Inc., for "Ramu and the Kite," adapted from *Ramu and the Kite* by Mehlli Gobhai. Copyright © 1968 by Prentice-Hall. Used by permission.

Rand McNally & Company, for "Undersea" by Marchette Chute, from *Child Life Magazine.* Copyright 1935, © 1963 by Rand McNally & Company. Used by permission.

Russell & Volkening, Inc., as agents for the author, for "Way Down Deep," from *Hello and Good-Bye* by Mary Ann Hoberman. Copyright © 1959 by Mary Ann Hoberman. Used by permission.

Scholastic Magazines, Inc., for *Charlie The Tramp,* by Russell Hoban. Copyright © 1966 by Russell Hoban. Used by permission.

Franklin Watts, Inc., for "Be Nice to Josephine," adapted from *Be Nice to Josephine* by Betty Horvath. Copyright © 1970 by Franklin Watts, Inc. Used by permission.

Albert Whitman & Co., for "Statues," from *Town and Countryside Poems* by John Travers Moore. Copyright © 1968. Used by permission.

World Publishing Company and The Bodley Head, Ltd., for "Fumio and the Dolphins," adapted from their translation of *Fumio and the Dolphins* by Chinoko Nakatani. Copyright © 1970 by The Bodley Head, Ltd. Used by permission.

Contents

The Earth We Live On

The Water All Around

The Sky Above

The Earth We Live On

The world is so full
    of a number of things,
I'm sure we should all
    be as happy as kings.

—Robert Louis Stevenson

13

Such Is the Way of the World

Benjamin Elkin

This was a big day for Desta. For the
first time he was to be in charge
of his father's cows all by himself. Desta was
singing as he walked along with the cows
and his pet monkey, Jima. All was right
with his world.

But the world does not stand still. Out of
nowhere came a big dog who jumped at Jima.
The monkey was so afraid, he climbed up a tree,
and just like that he was gone.

Desta was only a little boy, and he began to cry.
He cried so much that the cows began to run,
and soon they were gone, too. But Desta
didn't care about the cows. He only wanted
to find his pet monkey, Jima.

"Don't cry," said the owner of the dog. "Such
is the way of the world that dogs must hunt
and monkeys must run away. Here, you may have
this game to pay for your monkey," he said.
And he put the game under Desta's arm.

Down the road Desta saw some men sitting
around a fire. Maybe they knew where Jima was!
As Desta ran to the men, he tripped over one
of them who was sleeping near the fire. The game
fell out of his hands and into the fire.

The man got to his feet and said, "I should
not have been sleeping so near the fire. I'm
sorry about your game, but it did make our
fire much brighter. Such is the way
of the world. Here, you may have this pot
to pay for the game." And he put the pot
on Desta's head.

A quick look showed Desta that Jima wasn't there. "Maybe something horrible has happened to Jima," thought Desta. "I must not stand here. I must find him right away."

Desta ran until he came to a small town. Maybe Jima was there! Desta saw the men in the town getting ready for a hunt. All the men were wearing fur and feathers. But Desta did not see anyone with a pet monkey.

A man reached for the pot on Desta's head. "I don't have my drum," he said. "Stand here and let me drum on your pot."

But the man hit the pot only a few times
before it broke. "Such is the way of the world.
I have tried an army of pots, and not one has
ever made a good drum. I'm sorry I broke your
pot. Here, take this knife to pay for it."

Desta took the knife and went on looking
for Jima.

Along the way Desta stopped to watch a man
dig a hole with his hands. "I'm looking
for my pet monkey," he told the man. "Did you
see any monkeys today?"

"My boy," said the man, "when you watch goats,
you see only goats. Could I have your knife
for a minute to help me dig this hole?"

Desta gave the knife to the man, and he
started to dig. But the knife hit a stone
and broke.

"I'm very sorry," said the man. "But such
is the way of the world. Here, take this spear
to pay for the knife."

Desta took the spear. Now here was
something that might help him save Jima.
He saw some hunters ahead of him,
and he ran to ask them about his monkey.

A hunter at once reached out for Desta's spear.
"You must give us this spear. We saw a tiger
near our town, and we need all the spears
we can get. But first I want to try it out."

The spear was very old, and it broke when it hit
a tree.

"Such is the way of the world," said the hunter.
"It is far better to find out now that the spear
doesn't work than when we come face to face
with the tiger."

The man turned to Desta and said, "I'm sorry
I broke your spear. In this bag is a little monkey
that I found. Take the monkey for the spear.
The monkey will be a good pet for you."

"A little monkey," thought Desta. "Could it be Jima?"

Desta opened the bag, and there was his own Jima. He picked up the monkey and thought of nothing but the joy of having his pet back again.

But then, as Desta started for home, he remembered his father's cows. There they were ahead of him, going home without him. Desta ran after them.

Near the house Father and Mother looked up
and saw Desta bringing home the cows. And
walking beside Desta was his pet monkey, Jima.
Desta looked very happy. All was right
with his world.

Father turned to Mother and said, "We were
right to give Desta that little monkey.
There is nothing like a good pet to help a boy
do his work well. Such is the way of the world."

The Sunflower Garden

Janice May Udry

Pipsa was an Indian girl who lived in a village with her mother and father and five brothers. Four of the brothers were older than Pipsa, but one was still very little.

Pipsa's father was proud of how well her brothers could swim. He didn't notice how well Pipsa took care of her little brother. Her father was proud of how well her brothers fished. He didn't notice all the berries Pipsa picked.

Pipsa's father was proud of the way his sons trapped rabbits and birds. He didn't notice the beautiful straw bags that Pipsa made. And he didn't notice that now Pipsa helped her mother make clothes for the family.

Pipsa's father was like most fathers. He showed his sons how to do the things he did. He was proud of his sons and told them so again and again. But he never thought of telling his daughter how proud he was of her.

Pipsa's mother was proud of her and sometimes said, "You did well, my little Pipsa."

Every spring Pipsa helped her mother plant corn and beans. How her brothers loved to eat! But they never helped with the planting.

This year Pipsa couldn't wait for planting time to come. All winter she had been saving some special seeds in a little box. They were sunflower seeds she had picked in the fall when the family had gone to another village. That was the first time Pipsa had ever seen the big sunflowers growing.

One of the girls in the village showed Pipsa
some cakes that had been made from the seeds.
She told Pipsa that the seeds made wonderful
oil for the hair, too. Most of the girls of the
village put sunflower oil on their hair.

No one in Pipsa's village had ever thought of
growing sunflowers. But now that spring was here,
Pipsa was going to start a sunflower garden all
her own. Her mother wouldn't have time to help,
so Pipsa knew she would have to do all the
work herself.

One night before it got dark, Pipsa heard her
father say it would rain before morning.
Pipsa went out to the place she had picked
for her garden and planted the seeds.

After they were planted, Pipsa looked down
at the dirt covering the seeds. She asked herself,
"Are the seeds really any good? Did I plant them
right? Will they grow?"

Day after day Pipsa went to her garden and watched for a sign of green. And then one day she saw it! Soon the garden was filled with little plants reaching for the sun.

It was a good summer for growing. By the middle of the summer, most of the great sunflower heads were filled with seeds. Soon it would be time to pick them, and then Pipsa and her mother would make the cakes and the oil for their hair.

Mothers and children from Pipsa's village came to look at the big bright flowers. One of the plants was a giant sunflower "tree." It was three times as big as Pipsa.

Pipsa found that the birds loved her sunflowers, too. But she did her best to make them go away.

27

The Snake

One night when Pipsa was working in her garden, she heard a snake nearby. She put down her hoe and looked quickly for her little brother. He was playing and had not seen the snake.

Pipsa had to think fast. She had to keep that snake away from her brother. She picked up her hoe and walked quietly over to the snake. She had never seen a snake that big. She must kill it before it killed her brother. She had never been so afraid in all her life. What if she missed? What if she only made the snake mad?

Pipsa took the hoe and hit the snake on the back
of the head. Without stopping to see if she
had killed it, she hit the snake again
and again.

Pipsa's little brother was so afraid, he
jumped to his feet.

"Run, Little Brother, run!" cried Pipsa.

The little boy ran crying to his mother.
In a few minutes Pipsa's mother and father
and brothers came running. When her brothers saw
what had happened, they were surprised that such
a little girl could kill such a big snake.
For the first time Pipsa saw in their eyes
that they were proud of her.

And for the first time Pipsa's father said
to her, "You did well, my little daughter.
You are a brave child."

Pipsa's father looked around at the sunflower garden. He had never seen it before.

"What are you growing?" he asked.

"Sunflowers, Father," Pipsa told him.

"What are they for?" her father asked.

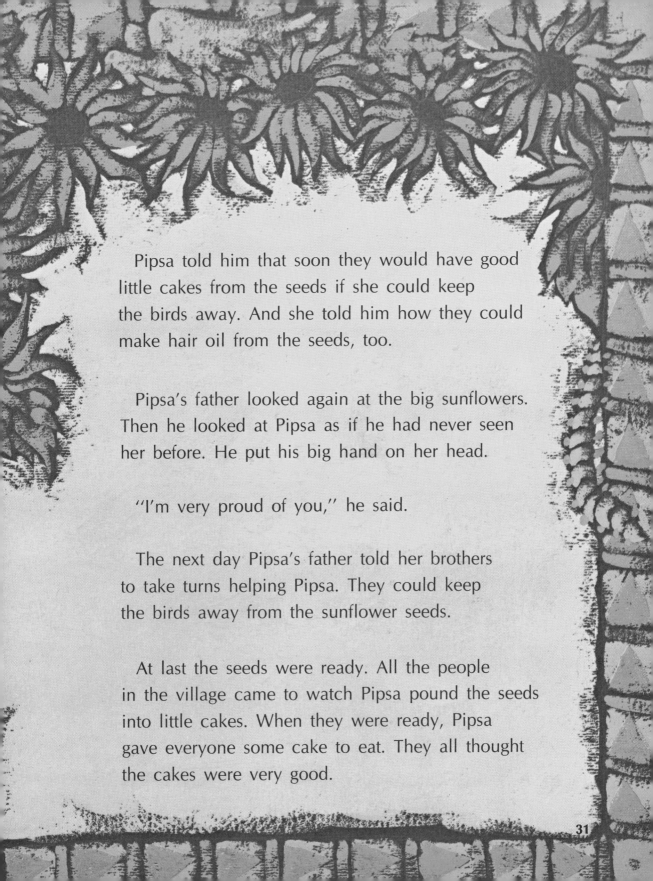

Pipsa told him that soon they would have good
little cakes from the seeds if she could keep
the birds away. And she told him how they could
make hair oil from the seeds, too.

Pipsa's father looked again at the big sunflowers.
Then he looked at Pipsa as if he had never seen
her before. He put his big hand on her head.

"I'm very proud of you," he said.

The next day Pipsa's father told her brothers
to take turns helping Pipsa. They could keep
the birds away from the sunflower seeds.

At last the seeds were ready. All the people
in the village came to watch Pipsa pound the seeds
into little cakes. When they were ready, Pipsa
gave everyone some cake to eat. They all thought
the cakes were very good.

Pipsa told the mothers that the oil from the
seeds would make their hair more beautiful. She
gave the people some seeds, and the next spring
they all grew sunflowers.

Everyone in the village was proud of the little
girl who gave a new plant and new ideas
to her people. They called her the "Sunflower Girl."

As the years went by, the Indians in Pipsa's village grew more and more sunflowers. Pipsa grew up and had a little girl of her own. But people still told of how Pipsa had started the first sunflower garden in their village.

And Pipsa's little brother never forgot that when he was very small, she had saved his life.

Frederick L. Olmstead

Elizabeth Levy

Do you have a park where you live? If you
do, did you ever think about how the park
got there? Your park didn't just happen
by itself. Someone had to think about it and
plan it.

Frederick L. Olmstead was a man who thought
about parks. He lived a long time ago —
before cars and before cities were as big
as they are now. But he knew that cities
would grow, and people would need parks —
beautiful parks, big parks. People would need
parks with a place to play baseball and a
place to walk in the hills — parks with trees
and flowers.

Frederick L. Olmstead planned some of the
most beautiful parks in our country and
maybe even in the world. But, for a long time,
Frederick's friends thought that he would
never really do anything.

"When is he going to stop fooling around?"
they would ask.

"I wish Frederick would find something to do."

Frederick went away to school, but he didn't
stay there. He worked in a store for a time,
but he didn't like that at all. He took a
trip to Europe, and he stayed away for a year.

When Frederick came home from Europe, he
went to work on a farm. He liked being a
farmer. His father was happy when Frederick
found something he liked to do. So he got
Frederick a farm of his own.

But Frederick didn't keep his farm for very
long. He began to think about Europe again.
And soon he took another trip there. This
time he wrote a book about his trip. One
of the things he wrote about was the parks he
had seen in some of the big cities in Europe.

When Frederick came back to this country,
he tried farming again. But once again
he didn't stay.

Frederick tried all kinds of work, but he
just couldn't find the one thing he really
wanted to do.

So Frederick went back to his home in New
York City. When he got there, some of his
friends were talking about making a very big
park in the city. When he heard about the
park, he said, "I'd like to have something
to do with that."

The city was holding a contest to see who
could plan the best park. So Olmstead and
a friend began working on a plan for the
contest. They thought about what people
would want in a park.

Should a walk in the park be like a walk
on a street, or should it be like a walk
in the forest? Should a park have places
for games like baseball? Should the park
have hills? Should there be a place to put
a monument in the park? Should there be
lots of little parks or one big one?

From his trips to Europe, Frederick knew
a lot about parks. And he knew a lot
about the country from being a farmer. He wanted
his park to be as beautiful as the ones he
had seen in Europe. And he wanted his park
to be like the country. So he and his friend
planned a park that would bring the country
to New York City.

Frederick and his friend won the contest.

Frederick's park is in New York City.
It's called Central Park. There are places
to play baseball and even places for a monument
or two. But most of all there are trees and hills
and even forests. You can walk off the city street,
and it's like being in the country.

You can play in Central Park, and you don't
have to look out for cars. You can go
to see bears in the park, and you don't have
to be afraid that a bear will bite you. You
can find flowers and trees, things to eat,
games to play, birds to feed, and benches
to sit on. Or you can just fall asleep in the sun.
Central Park has something for everyone.

People all over the country saw what a
wonderful place Central Park turned out
to be. So they asked Frederick to plan parks for
their cities. And he did. Today there are parks by
Frederick Olmstead in all parts of our country.

Frederick Olmstead worked on park plans
for the rest of his life. And never again
did anyone ask, "When is Frederick going
to stop fooling around?"

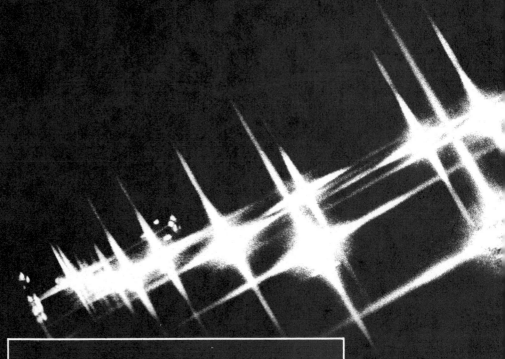

Statues

I wonder what happens after dark
  to statues in the park.
Do they dance and sing
  in the joy of spring?
Do they run and play
  till the light of day?
I wonder what happens to statues
  in the park.

—*John Travers Moore*

Be Nice to Josephine

Betty Horvath

Charlie loved Saturday. He couldn't wait
for Saturday to come so he could play baseball
with his friends. The only time they didn't
play was when it rained or was cold. The boys
would meet outside the school and play baseball
all day, stopping only for lunch.

Today was Saturday, and the sun was out.
It was a good day for baseball. Just as Charlie
was getting ready to leave, he heard the
telephone ring.

Charlie could hear his mother talking on the telephone. "How wonderful," she said. "I can't *wait* to see you."

When she came back into the room, Charlie's mother had her "I've-got-to-hurry" look. "That was my cousin Ellen on the telephone," she said. "She's in town with her little girl, and they're coming to see us."

"That's nice," said Charlie.

"They'll be here soon," said Charlie's mother. "I've got to hurry." She took the food off the table and began cleaning up.

Charlie thought this was a good time to leave. He picked up his bat and was just about to the door when his mother said, "I'll need your help today, Charlie."

"All right," said Charlie. "What can I do?
Take out the garbage? Get some food at the
store? Clean my room?"

"No," she said. "Nothing like that. Ellen is
bringing her little girl, Josephine. I want you
to be nice to Josephine. Think of something
the two of you can do for the day."

"Josephine? A girl?
And I have to be nice to her all day?

Why?
Why?
Why?" asked Charlie.

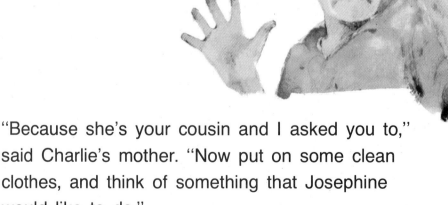

"Because she's your cousin and I asked you to,"
said Charlie's mother. "Now put on some clean
clothes, and think of something that Josephine
would like to do."

"I know what she'd like to do," thought Charlie. "She'd like to play dolls or have a tea party."

His day was ruined. What if the gang saw him playing with a *girl?* He'd never hear the last of it.

"I'll have to hide her," he thought. "But where could you hide anything as big as a girl? I know! I'll take her on a picnic."

He thought about picnics for a minute. He thought about food. Then he thought about girls. Then he began to laugh. "I'll bet she's never been on a picnic like *this* before. We might even go fishing," he said to himself.

Charlie was making sandwiches when Ellen and Josephine came to the house.

"Where's Charlie?" asked Josephine.

"He's making sandwiches," said Charlie's mother. "Hurry up, Charlie. Your cousins are here."

"Coming!" said Charlie. He put the sandwiches into the lunch bag and went into the living room to meet his cousins.

"Charlie's taking Josephine on a picnic," said Charlie's mother.

"Oh, good," said Josephine.

"How nice," said Cousin Ellen.

As Charlie and Josephine were about to leave, Charlie's mother said, "Come home before it gets dark."

"She didn't have to tell me *that*," Charlie thought. "I plan to get rid of Josephine as soon as I can."

The Picnic

Charlie got two fishing poles and a box and
gave them to Josephine. He took the long way
to the stream so he wouldn't have to go near
the school. He'd be ruined if the gang saw him
with Josephine.

As they walked along, Charlie waited for Josephine
to start laughing and acting like a girl.
Then he could forget about being nice to her
and tell her she'd ruined his Saturday. He wished
she'd hurry up and start acting like a girl.

When Charlie and Josephine got to the stream,
Josephine put the fishing poles down
and opened the box.

"Can I dig the worms?" she asked Charlie.

Charlie just looked at her. "I was just about
to ask you to do that," he said. "Do you really
like worms?"

"Well," said Josephine. "I like snakes better. But worms will do." She found something to dig with, took her hat off, filled it with dirt, and began looking for worms.

Charlie just watched her. He couldn't think of a thing to say. So far, the picnic wasn't turning out at all the way he had planned.

"Are you sure you wouldn't rather be playing dolls?" Charlie asked.

"No, I wouldn't," Josephine said as she dropped a worm into her hat. "But if you want to, I will."

"Forget it," said Charlie.

Soon it was time for lunch. Charlie opened the lunch bag. He took out a ham sandwich for himself and handed the other sandwich to Josephine.

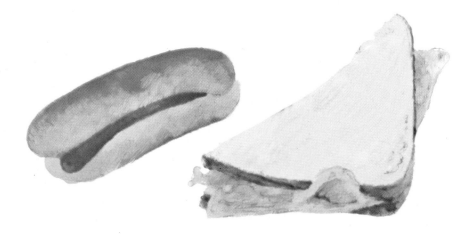

"What is it?" she asked.

"Hot dog and jam," he said quietly.

"I've never had that before," she said.

"You can have the ham sandwich if you'd rather,"
said Charlie.

"No," said Josephine. "I've had ham lots
of times. Hot dog and jam will be different.
Did you make the sandwich just for me?"

"I sure did," said Charlie.

"You're nice," said Josephine.

After lunch they picked up their fishing poles and began to fish. Charlie was surprised that Josephine could bait her own hook. "She's different from the girls I know," thought Charlie. "If I have to spend the day with a girl, it might as well be Josephine."

"Do you ever play baseball?" Josephine asked.

"Sometimes," said Charlie, who hadn't missed a Saturday game in two years.

"You're different from the boys I know," said Josephine. "Most of them would rather play baseball than go fishing with a girl."

"Oh, well," said Charlie. "I like to do something different now and then." It wasn't what he had planned to say at all.

Time went on, and the sun began to set. Charlie jumped up and said, "We'd better hurry if we're going to get home before dark."

They dumped the dirt out of Josephine's hat and put the hooks back in the box. Charlie picked up the fishing poles and the box and the lunch bag, and they started for home.

"Want me to take something?" Josephine asked.

"No, thanks," said Charlie. "I've got everything."

"We're going home a different way," Josephine noticed.

"Yes," said Charlie. "We don't have time to go the long way. I'll show you where I go to school." Charlie was sure the baseball game would be over, and his friends would be gone.

But when Charlie and Josephine got to the school, they could hear noise. The ball game was still going on. There was the gang—Jimmy, Max, George, and Happy.

"Look, gang, there's Charlie," called George. "Where have you been all day, Charlie?"

"Who's your girl, Charlie?" asked Happy.

"She's not my girl," said Charlie. "She's my cousin Josephine."

"You missed all the fun," said Max. "Did you have to spend all day with her?"

Charlie looked down at Josephine. She looked kind of little. And she really looked sad. Someone had better be nice to Josephine fast. He heard himself say another thing that he hadn't planned to say.

"No, I didn't *have* to spend all day with her," said Charlie. "I *wanted* to. She's my cousin. Come on, Josephine. Let's go home."

Sun.	Mon.	Tues.	Wed.	Thurs.	Fri.	Sat.
		1	2	3	4	5
6	7	8	9	10	11	12
13	14	15	16	17	18	19
20	21	22	23	24	25	26
27	28	29	30	31		

May Days

If today were May 9, what day of the week would it be?

If your birthday were May 14, would it be a school day?

If you went on a picnic May 31, what day of the week would that be?

Charlie plays ball on May 5, 12, 19, and 26. On what day of the week does he play ball?

Lucy's class has music every Friday. How many times will they have music this month?

On May 1, Ellen went to the doctor's. He said to come back in a week. What day was that?

Every Sunday Josephine has a chicken dinner at her grandmother's. On what dates will she have chicken dinners in May?

Calendar Reading. Have the children examine and discuss the calendar above. Then have the questions read and answered. Point out that our writing system employs numerals in many kinds of charts and graphs.

Martin for Mayor

Helene Hanff

One night Butch Martin's father said,
"They want me to run for mayor."

"How wonderful!" said Butch's mother.

"It will mean a lot of work this fall,"
said Mr. Martin.

"I'll help you," said Butch.

"Now, Butch," said his mother. "We know you
mean well. But you know that every time you
try to help, something happens."

"What do you mean?" asked Butch.

"Do you remember the time you surprised
me by bringing my groceries home
from the store?" asked Butch's mother.
"You came home with another lady's groceries.
She had to run all over town before she found
her groceries."

"I think you should wait until you're a little
older to work in an election campaign," said
Butch's father.

"If Dad doesn't want my help, then he can just
get elected mayor by himself," thought Butch.

But a few days after that, Butch's father took him downtown to a store. There was a big sign in the window that said, "Martin for Mayor."

"Come in," said Butch's father, "and see my campaign headquarters."

When they went into the headquarters, Butch noticed signs all over the tables. Newspapers, boxes of straw hats, and campaign buttons were in every corner of the room.

"What are all these people doing here?" Butch asked his father.

"These people are working to get me elected," said Butch's father.

"May I help?" asked Butch.

"Sure," said a girl named Ann, who was sitting at a table folding letters.

"Now, Butch," said his father. "You know that every time you try to help, something happens."

"Oh, nothing will happen," said Ann. "He can help me fold these letters."

"All right," said Butch's father. Then he and the others went off to a meeting.

Butch and Ann worked together all morning folding letters. The letters were going to be mailed to everyone in town, asking them to vote for Butch's father for mayor. When it was time for lunch, Ann said, "I'll go next door and get us something to eat."

"I'll go for you," said Butch.

"No, thank you," said Ann. "I haven't been out all morning. I'd like to get some air."

When Ann had gone, Butch said, "It's hot in here. I'll air out the room the way my mother does at home." He opened the back door, and turned on a big fan that was standing in one corner of the room. And all at once letters, newspapers, and signs started to fly around the room.

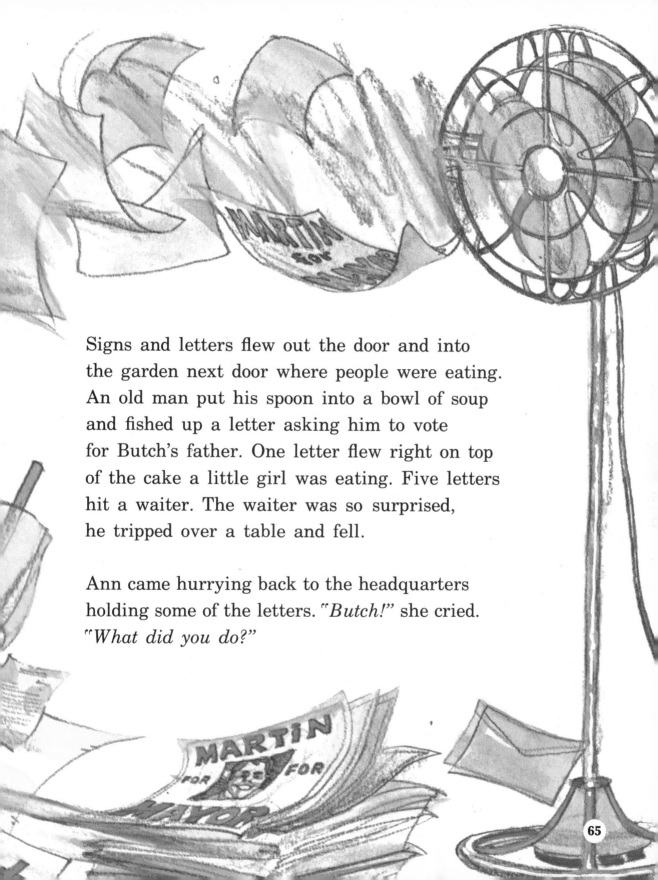

Signs and letters flew out the door and into
the garden next door where people were eating.
An old man put his spoon into a bowl of soup
and fished up a letter asking him to vote
for Butch's father. One letter flew right on top
of the cake a little girl was eating. Five letters
hit a waiter. The waiter was so surprised,
he tripped over a table and fell.

Ann came hurrying back to the headquarters
holding some of the letters. *"Butch!"* she cried.
"What did you do?"

Just then the people from the garden came running into the headquarters. They all started yelling at Butch at once.

"I was only trying to help," said Butch.

"*Help!*" cried the owner of the garden. "Just stay away from my garden."

When the people had gone back to the garden, Ann closed the door and turned to Butch. "I'm sorry, Butch," she said. "I'm afraid you're not ready to work on an election campaign. I'll do the letters myself."

Butch was sad as he walked home. It was the
same old story all over again. Every time he
tried to help someone, something happened.

Butch Elects a Mayor

School started, and Butch forgot about his
father's campaign. But the day before the
election, Butch happened to walk by his father's
headquarters. Ann was at the window,
and she came out to say hello.

"Are you coming to the rally tonight?"
she asked.

"No," said Butch.

"Oh, please come," said Ann. "It's going
to be in the big hall on Spring Street. Lots
of people will be there to hear your father make
his big speech. He's going to tell them all the
wonderful things he wants to do for the city.
Then they'll vote for him."

That night the big hall was filled with people. Butch's father walked out on the stage and up to the microphone. Everyone grew quiet. Butch's father began his speech.

"We can't hear you,"

someone yelled from the back of the hall.

Two men ran up on the stage to look at the microphone. It wasn't working! Butch thought for a minute. "Maybe the microphone wasn't plugged in. I'd better go and help."

Butch got up quickly and ran to the wall where the microphone was plugged in. He took out the plug and tried to put it in another outlet. The plug didn't fit, but Butch tried again and again. And then it happened—

ALL THE LIGHTS WENT OUT IN THE HALL!

"Lights!" everyone cried.
"Turn on the lights!"

A big man came up to Butch in the dark and saw the plug in Butch's hand. "Some little boy was fooling with the plugs!" he called out.

Ann and her friend Bert came hurrying over.

"Butch! What did you do?" they cried.

"He broke up the rally, that's what he did,"
said the big man. "We'll never get these
lights back on tonight."

"But it's the night before the election!"
said Ann. "What about Mr. Martin's speech?"

"He can't make a speech in the dark," said
the big man. "Besides, people are leaving."

The man was right. Everyone was trying
to find the door. Within a few minutes
all the people were gone. The rally was over.

On the way home, Butch's mother and father didn't say anything to him at all. When they got home, Butch's father went for a walk, and his mother went into the house. Butch stayed outside and began to feel sorry for himself. He tried not to cry.

Just then a man came by and asked Butch if his father was home.

"He went for a walk," said Butch.

"You don't look very happy," said the man. "Did something happen?"

Butch told the man the story about the times he had tried to help his father in the campaign. Then he said, "And tonight no one heard my father's speech. They won't know all the things he wanted to do for the city. They won't vote for him. He won't be elected mayor." Then he began to cry.

"Don't be so sad," the man told Butch.
"You'll find things looking much brighter
in the morning. Good night." The man went off
down the street, and Butch went to bed
still feeling sad.

The next morning Butch was the
first one up. The first thing he
did was get the newspaper. When
he opened it up, he was surprised
to see his picture on the first
page.

Under the picture it said,

Butch Martin Tries to Help

And under that was the story
Butch had told the man
the night before.

The man wrote for the newspaper.
He had put Butch's father's speech
in the paper, too. Everyone could read it
and know all the things he wanted to do
for the city.

"Butch," said his father after reading the
story. "I don't want you to feel bad if I'm
not elected."

Butch went to the school with his mother and
father that morning and waited for them to vote.
A man with a newspaper came over
to Butch and said, "So this is the boy I've been
reading about! If your father gets elected,
it will be because of you." Other people came
over and said the same thing to Butch.

That night Butch's father found out
he had won the election.

"You know," said Butch's father the next morning, "now that I've won, I'm a little afraid. It's going to be a big job being mayor of this city."

"I'll help you," said Butch.

And this time his mother and father didn't say anything!

The Apple War

Bernice Myers

"They're my apples,"
said King Sam.

"They're on my tree,"
said King Oscar.

"But the apples
fall over
on my land!"
said King Sam.

"The apples
are on
MY tree,
and MY tree
stands on
MY land!"
yelled King Oscar.

"The apples
may be on
your tree,
but they all
FALL
on my land,"
said King Sam.
"So
they are MY APPLES!"

"They're *not!*"
said King Oscar.

"They *are!*"
said King Sam.

"*Not!*"
said King Oscar.

"*Are!*"
said King Sam.
"*Are, are, are!*
This means war.
And I mean
WAR!"

"I'm ready any time,"
said King Oscar.

"How's May 5?
It falls on a Tuesday,"
said King Sam.

"Good,"
said King Oscar.
"I'll see you then."

On the morning of May 4
King Sam called for
William.
"Find out if King Oscar
is ready
for our war.
Tomorrow is May 5!"

"But, King!
You can't have a war
tomorrow.
It's your birthday!"
said William.

"You're right.
I forgot!
But I can't call off
a war
at the last minute.
A promise is a promise."

"And, King,"
said William,
"you always have
a party
on your birthday.
We've already asked
everyone to come."

King Sam was upset.
He wanted to keep his promise.
But he didn't know
what
to do.

"I know," he said.
"I'll hide!"

"A king doesn't hide,"
said William.

"Then I'll run away,"
said King Sam.

"A king never runs away,"
said William.

"Then say I'm sick,
or my aunt is sick,
or I broke my leg,"
said King Sam.

William acted as if
he didn't hear.

"William,
William.
What will I do?"
King Sam asked.

"Well,"
said William,
"have the war first
and then
your birthday party.
Or,
have your birthday party
and then the war."

"Great idea," said
King Sam.
"I'll have the party
and then the war.
No. No.
The war and then the party.
Oh, I can't make up my mind
now.
I'm going to sleep.
I can think better
in the morning."

The next day
when King Sam got up,
he began to think.
He walked
around and around.
Sometimes he waved
his arms in the air.
At last
he made up his mind.

"I'll get the war over
quickly
and still have time for my
birthday party."
He jumped on his horse,
and off he went
to the battlefield.

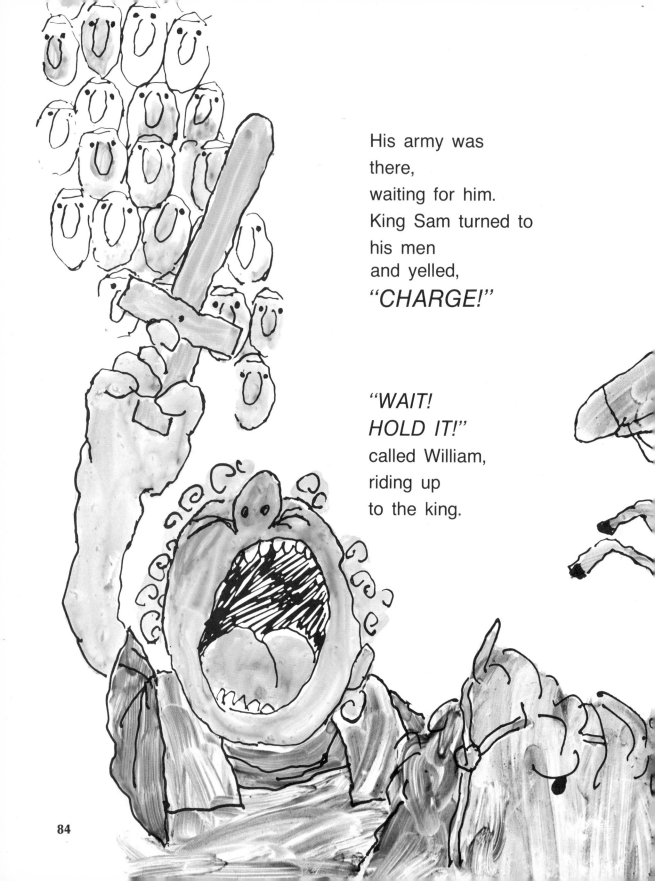

His army was
there,
waiting for him.
King Sam turned to
his men
and yelled,
"CHARGE!"

*"WAIT!
HOLD IT!"*
called William,
riding up
to the king.

"If you have the war
first,
you might not have
anyone at
your party."

"Good thinking,
William,"
said King Sam.

"So we'll have
the party
first
and then the war!"

King Oscar waved
from the other side of
the battlefield.

King Sam waved back.
"We'll fight
this afternoon, Oscar."

"We're going to have
my party first,"
said King Sam.

And right there
in the middle of the
battlefield,
the tables were set,
and everyone began to
eat
and laugh
and sing
and play and . . .

They were having such a
good time
that no one wanted to
fight
anymore.

"You still mad?"
asked King Sam.

"No. You mad?"
asked King Oscar.

by birthday to you happy

87

"*Me? Mad?*
Why should I be mad?"
asked King Sam.

"Then what were we
going to fight about?"
asked King Oscar.

"I forgot,"
said King Sam.

With that
the two kings
looked at each other
and began to
laugh.

When the army heard
that there would be
no war,
they yelled,
"OH, GOOD!"

"Come see me
sometime,"
said King Sam.
"I'm having a get-together
tomorrow.
Why don't you come
and bring
the family?"

"Thanks.
I will,"
said King Oscar.
"I like your shoes
by the way.
Who's your cobbler?"

"I'll have some
made
for you
if you like,"
said King Sam.

"Here.
Have one of my
apples," said King Oscar.

"*Your* apples?"
said King Sam.

91

Where Do Words Come From?

Many of our words are made by putting together words or parts of words from other languages. Words like *microscope, microphone, telescope,* and *telephone* are made this way.

Tele means *far away.*
Phone means *sound.*
Scope means *see.*
Micro means *small* or
  making small things large.

What do we use to speak with people far away?
What do we use to see something far away?
What do we use to see very small things?
What do we use to make our voices louder?

Word Derivations. Have the first paragraph read and the Greek roots discussed. Then have the questions answered.

VALENTINE FOR EARTH

Oh, it will be fine
To rocket through space
And see the reverse
Of the moon's dark face,

To travel to Saturn
Or Venus or Mars,
Or maybe discover
Some uncharted stars.

But do they have anything
Better than we?
Do you think, for instance,
They have a blue sea

For sailing and swimming?
Do planets have hills
With raspberry thickets
Where a song sparrow fills

The summer with music?
And do they have snow
To silver the roads
Where the school buses go?

Oh, I'm all for rockets
And worlds cold or hot,
But I'm wild in love
With the planet we've got!

—Frances Frost

The Water All Around

Until I Saw the Sea

Until I saw the sea
I did not know
that wind
could wrinkle water so.

I never knew
that sun
could splinter a whole sea of blue.

Nor did I know before
a sea breathes in and out upon a shore.

— Lilian Moore

Fumio and the Dolphins

Chinoko Nakatani

Fumio lived in a small village by the sea.
When he was not in school, Fumio liked
to spend his time fishing or swimming.

Fumio's father and brother were fishermen.
They caught many kinds of fish. Sometimes
in the fall they caught dolphins that swam
after the fish and came near the shore.

One day Fumio went fishing with his brother
Taro. As they went by the rocky waters near
the lighthouse, Fumio saw something moving
in the water.

"Taro! Look over there!" There it was again,
a fin coming out of the water.
Then a head popped up.

"It's a dolphin, Fumio,"
Taro said.

97

The boys threw a fish to the dolphin, and
at once another head popped up. Fumio cried,
"It's a baby dolphin. The big one is its mother."

The mother dolphin jumped out of the water
and caught the fish. Then the baby dolphin
jumped for a fish, too. Into the air went
the two dolphins as Fumio threw them fish,
one after another.

When Taro saw how many fish were gone,
he said, "We must keep the rest. We have
to eat, too. Let's come back tomorrow."

The next afternoon, as soon as he got home
from school, Fumio ran to the shore. Just then
someone called, "The dolphins are coming in!"
All the fishermen ran to their boats.

When he saw the men and the boats going after the dolphins, Fumio began to worry. Where were his two special dolphins? Would they be caught?

Fumio ran to Taro. "I'm afraid that our dolphins will be caught," he said.

"Don't worry. I'm sure they will stay in back of the rocks," said Taro. "When the boats come back, we will go and look for them."

At last the boats came back into sight.
Fumio saw the fishermen beat the water with
long poles to move the dolphins into the shore.
When the dolphins were near the shore, the
fishermen threw out their nets and caught them.
Fumio was still worried about the baby dolphin
and its mother. He was sure they had
been caught.

Fumio ran to the nets, looking at each dolphin
in turn. But they all looked just alike, and he
could not find his special friends.

Then Fumio and Taro set out to look for their
dolphins, taking lots of fish with them.

Fumio hit the side of the boat to call the dolphins, but there was no sign of them. It was starting to grow dark.

At last Taro said, "They must have been caught. Let's go home, Fumio."

But just then they saw two fins cut through the water. "There they are!" called Fumio. "The mother dolphin and her baby are safe after all!"

Fumio threw fish to the two dolphins, and Taro headed the boat out to the open sea.

"We'll lead the dolphins far away, so they will never be caught," said Taro.

The dolphins swam far, far out until they could no longer be seen in the night sea.

Fumio and Taro turned for home.

My Mother Talks to Dolphins

Elizabeth Levy

My name is Penny, and I'm ten years old. Today
my teacher said we had to write a story called
"What I Want to Be."

That's not hard for me.

What I Want to Be

   I want to be a scientist like my mother.
My mother talks to dolphins.
Don't think I'm being funny. She really
is a scientist, and she really does talk
to dolphins. She once lived with a dolphin
because she wanted to teach it to talk.
   Scientists think that dolphins
can talk because they have such big brains.
Dolphins have brains just as big as ours.

   My mother says that dolphins seem to talk
to each other just as people do. Maybe you
think that lots of animals talk to each other.
Cats mee—ow, birds sing—what's so special
about the noises a dolphin makes?

Mother has seen dolphins do something that cats or birds never do. She's seen a sick dolphin whistle to other dolphins for help, and the other dolphins come to it. She could hear the dolphins making noises just as if they were doctors asking the sick dolphin how sick it was.

After a lot of noise, the dolphins seemed to come up with a plan. They had to bring food to the sick dolphin until it was well. Mother and other scientists thought that when the dolphins made noise, they were really talking it over, the way people might do if they had to help someone.

My mother says that it will take time
for scientists to find out if dolphins
can really talk. That is what she
is trying to do.

When dolphins are together, they make
sounds that are not at all like the sounds
you or I make. Most of the time they make
whistle sounds through the hole in their heads.

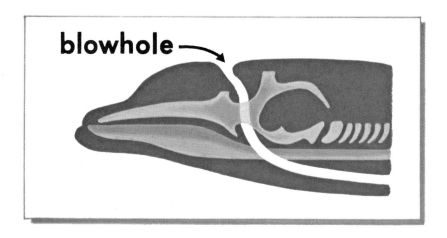

But when a dolphin is caught, he'll try
to make sounds like the people around him. My
mother and other scientists seem to think that
the dolphins are trying to talk to us. Maybe
they're asking the people who caught them
to let them go. No one knows. But scientists
are trying to think of ways to teach dolphins
to talk.

One day my mother and her friends thought,
"Why not teach a dolphin to talk the same way
we teach babies to talk?" I don't remember
my mother teaching me to talk, but she says
she did.

Mothers are around their babies a lot, and
mothers talk to their babies all the time.
Most people like to talk to a baby, so a baby
is always hearing words.

Soon the baby starts to make sounds that
aren't words but sound like words. This is
baby talk. Then, when the baby is a little
older, the baby starts to say real words.

Mother thinks that when dolphins are caught
and make the sounds of the people around them,
they are talking baby talk. She thinks
that if a dolphin could be around people
all the time, the dolphin might start to talk.

The scientists made a special pool where
my mother and the dolphin lived together.
The pool had a room for my mother to cook in
and a bed where she could sleep.

When my mother went to live in the pool,
I didn't get to go with her. I went to stay
with my father in Washington. But when
I got home, my mother told me all about it.

My mother and the dolphin played all the time.
It loved to play ball. Every time my mother
would throw the ball, she'd say "ball,"
and soon the dolphin learned to say "ball."
The dolphin might have learned other words,
but it was hard for my mother to understand
the sounds the dolphin made.

Remember dolphins talk to each other
in whistles, and it's very hard for them
to make any people sounds at all through
the hole in their heads.

As you can see, I know a lot about dolphins. I find that it helps me in school. If the teacher wants to know what I did last summer, I can tell her about the times my mother let me swim and play with her dolphins.

Or, if we have to write something, I can always write:

"Dolphins in the sea
I wish they'd talk to me . . ."

The only thing is that about the middle of last year, my teacher told me she wanted to hear about something other than dolphins.

But this is the start of a new school year, and I have a new teacher who doesn't know anything about dolphins.

The Shell Collection

Dina Anastasio

Every day, when the sand was hot from the morning sun, the boy ran down to the water to play. He loved the mornings. Very few people were on the beach, and he could swim and play by himself.

Sometimes an old man came to the beach and sat near the water. But he was very quiet, and the boy soon forgot that he was there.

After lunch the older children ran down the
road and onto the sand, laughing and calling
to each other. Then the quiet beach was filled
with their noise. The children teased the boy,
for he was very small and could not do
the things they did.

One day they teased him because he could not
swim far out in the water. The boy looked down
the beach at the old man. The old man had been
watching the children, and he smiled when the
boy turned.

The boy walked down the beach to the
place where the old man sat in his chair.

"Hello," the boy said as he sat on the sand
beside the chair. "My name is Sandy."

"And I'm Bernard,"
said the old man quietly.

Every day after that, the boy sat near the old man.
As the weeks went by, they became good friends.
When the older children teased the boy, the old
man smiled and said, "Soon you will be bigger,
and you will swim very well. Then the children
will not tease you."

One morning, when the boy came to the beach,
the old man handed him an old box. When he
opened it, the boy saw a collection of seashells.
He picked them up one by one and turned
them over and over in his hands. One shell was
bright red and very beautiful, and when the boy
put it to his ear, he could hear the sea.

"I found this shell far away, on a beach very much like this one," the old man told the boy. "It was many years ago, and I thought it was the most beautiful thing in the world."

Then the man showed the boy the book he had with him that day. It was a book about seashells, and on every page there were beautiful pictures of shells. They found a picture of the red shell, and the old man read its story to the boy.

After that day the boy spent his afternoons looking for shells in the sand. And the older children laughed and yelled far out in the water.

At first he found only small white shells on
the beach. But as the weeks went by, he began
to find lovely pink, brown, and red shells
for his collection. Whenever he found one,
he took it to Bernard. The old man looked it up
in his book and read to the boy about the new shell.

For a few weeks the old man told the boy where
to look for the shells. But as the collection grew,
the boy came to know where they were. Then he
no longer needed help.

A Shell for Sandy

One day, while the boy walked slowly along
the hot sand looking for shells, he kicked over
a big black stone. There, where the stone had been,
lay the most beautiful pink shell that the boy had
ever seen. He picked it up and ran down
the beach to his friend.

Bernard turned the shell over and over
in his hand. Then he picked up his shell book
and looked through the pages very quickly until
he found the one he wanted. He showed the page
to the boy, and they looked at it together.
There were many shells much like Sandy's,
but not one was just like it. Slowly they went
through every page of the shell book.

"I think," said Bernard happily, "that you have
found a very special and new shell. As you
can see, there are many like it in the book, but not
one is just like yours. But to be sure, we
will go to the museum this afternoon and look
at their collection of shells. Then if we don't
find one like yours, we will show it
to the scientist at the museum. He will tell us
if you have found a new shell."

After lunch the boy ran down to the beach
to meet the old man, and together they walked
into town. When they got to the museum, they
asked to see the shell collection. A lady led them
into a room with cases and cases of shells.
The old man and the boy walked slowly
around the room and looked at every shell.
But they could not find the boy's shell,
and so they asked to see the scientist.

When the boy showed him his shell,
the scientist said, "I have never
seen a shell just like this. It could be
a new kind of shell that no one
has ever found before. Where did you find it?"

"Under a black stone on the beach,"
said Sandy.

"Will you show me?" asked the scientist.

The old man and the boy led the scientist down
to the beach, and the boy showed him the black
stone. "That's where I first saw the shell,"
said the boy.

The older children walked behind the scientist
while he looked through the sand. When they asked
him what he was doing, he told them about
the boy's new shell.

"If Sandy has really found a new kind of shell,"
the scientist said, "he can name it whatever he
wishes."

After a few weeks the scientist called the boy and said, "It looks as if you have really found a special shell. Come to the museum when you have thought of a name for it."

That night the boy could not sleep. He lay in his bed thinking of names for his shell, but he was not happy with any of them. When at last he fell asleep, he still had not made up his mind what to name his shell.

The noon sun was hot in the sky when the boy got to the beach the next day. But the old man was not yet there. While the boy waited for his friend, he lay on the sand. The older children stopped to say hello and to ask about his shell.

"What do you think I should name my shell?" the boy asked.

"Name it *Bobby*," laughed a boy named Bobby. "That's a good name."

"Name it *Peter*," said his brother.

"No, no, name it *Ed!*" called Ed.

"How about *George*?" yelled a boy named George.

But Sandy didn't like any of the names the older children thought of.

All at once the boy jumped quickly to his feet and ran down the beach to wait for the old man. He had thought of a wonderful name for his shell. When he saw his friend walking slowly near the water, he ran to meet him. He asked the old man to go with him to the museum to see the scientist. Together they walked up the beach and into the town.

At the museum the boy saw the scientist. "I would like to name my shell after Bernard," he said, "because Bernard is my friend."

"That is a good name," said the scientist. "The shell will be called

Conus bernardi."

The old man smiled
and took the boy's hand,
and together they walked
back to the sea.

The Collector

I have a collection
Of bottles and sticks,
Of seashells and small bells
And baubles and bricks,

Of spiders and gliders
And crayons and cans,
Of kite string and fly wings
And red rubber bands.

Hangers and twangers
And wires that connect
Are some more of the things
That I like to collect.

—Marci Ridlon

Words Grow!

You can make some words grow by adding an ending.

collect + ion = collection

If you **collect** things, you will have a **collection.**

elect + ion = election

If you want to **elect** someone, you must have an **election.**

direct + ion = direction

If you **direct** someone, you send them in the right **direction.**

What other words end with *ion?*

Suffix *ion.* Have the page read. Discuss the change in structure and meaning when *-ion* is added to the base words.

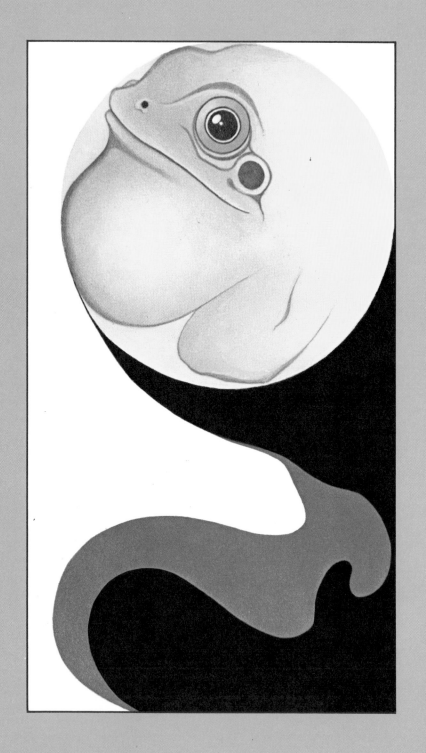

The Frog That Swallowed the Ocean

One night, long ago, a boy and his grandfather sat by a village campfire. As the boy looked up at the moon, he thought he saw a giant frog.

"Grandfather," said the boy, "is that the frog that once swallowed the ocean?"

"Yes, my child," said the grandfather. "But the frog you see in the moon tonight wasn't always a frog. It was once a Great Spirit that watched over the world."

"Tell me the story, Grandfather," said the boy.

As the people from the village sat down by the campfire, the grandfather began to tell the story.

A Great Spirit looked down upon the earth and said, "You, Earth, will be covered with many green plants. You will be covered with flowers and trees. Birds will sit in your trees, and bees will come to your flowers. Many animals will live on your land."

Then the Great Spirit turned to the ocean and said, "You, Great Ocean, will cover much of this world. Your waters will be wide, and the voice of your waves will be loud on the shore.

"But take care, Ocean! Take care that you stay in your own part of the world. Do not let your waters roll up too far on the shore. Do you understand me? And do you promise to do what I say?"

"I understand, Great Spirit," said the ocean, "and I will do as you say."

So, when the ocean waves broke on the shore, they quickly rolled back where they belonged.

But in time the ocean grew too proud. Its waves began to roll farther and farther up on the shore. Flowers and trees were ruined by the seawater. The animals ran into the forests. Some climbed up on the rocks and into the treetops.

Every day the ocean rolled farther and farther up on the land. Some animals were swallowed up by the waves. The animals that were still safe called to the Great Spirit.

The Great Spirit came down from the sky. When he saw what the ocean was doing, he was filled with anger. He said to the ocean in a loud voice, "You did not keep your promise. It was not enough that you should own more of the world than I gave to the earth. You thought you could own all of it.

"You will be sorry for what you did.

"All your water and all the waters that feed you will be seen no more. They will not come back again until I forget my anger."

Just then a giant frog came down from the sky and . . .

swallowed up the ocean from its bed.

When the boy heard this part of the story, he thought to himself, *"What would the world be like without water? How could plants grow? How would men and animals on land get water? And what would become of the fish in the sea?"*

"Was there no water at all in the world then, Grandfather?" the boy asked.

"How can I say, my child?" said his grandfather. "I was not there. There may have been some water in the streams, but the Great Spirit said the ocean would have no more water."

A Good Idea

The grandfather went on with the story. He told how all the animals got together on the dry shore. The fish were there, and the birds, too. They talked of how they could make the Great Spirit forget his anger and bring the ocean waters back to the world.

"I can see the frog in the moon," said a little bear from the treetop. "He keeps his mouth closed."

"That frog must be the Great Spirit," said a laughing bird. "If we can make the frog laugh, he will forget his anger. He will open his mouth when he laughs, and the ocean waters will come out."

"I will try first," said the laughing bird. "I will laugh and laugh. Maybe the frog will laugh with me."

The other animals thought this was a good idea. After all, who should know better about laughing than a laughing bird?

The big brown bird began to laugh. The laugh
was so loud, it must have reached the moon. If
the giant frog heard it, he made no sign. His
mouth did not open. His face did not move.

"I can laugh as loud as that," said a dog.
He opened his mouth and laughed as loud
as he could. Still the face of the frog did not move,
and his mouth did not open.

One after the other, the animals and birds and
the fish, too, tried to make the frog laugh.

Two kangaroos stood up on their tails and began jumping around. But that did not seem funny at all to the frog in the moon.

A giant turtle stood up on its back legs and began to walk around. The animals thought that this would surely make the frog laugh. But it did not. The frog's mouth was still closed.

Two dolphins jumped up in the air on the dry bed of the sea again and again. They, too, smiled at the frog. But the frog's mouth did not open.

"Let us try, too," cried two eels. "Maybe we can make the frog laugh so that he will forget his anger."

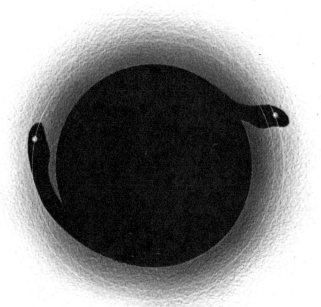

The two eels went around and around so fast
that soon they were tied in a knot. They were tied
in a knot so tight there was no way they could get
out of it. Never had there been such turning
and moving about.

When the animals saw the eels, they began
to laugh. Then there came a cry from the treetop.
It was the bear. *"The giant frog smiled,"*
he said. *"Look! Look at his face! The frog
in the moon is about to laugh!"*

And then it happened.

The frog forgot his anger and began to laugh.
His mouth opened, and the waters of the world
came streaming out. The ocean once more lay in
its own bed. Clear water filled the streams and
lakes and ponds. Men and animals of the world
were overcome with joy.

Sometimes, even today, the big waves try to roll over the land. But the ocean remembers the Great Spirit's anger and quickly pulls the waves back.

Undersea

Beneath the waters
　Green and cool
The mermaids keep
　A swimming school.

The oysters trot;
　The lobsters prance;
The dolphins come
　To join the dance.

But the jellyfish
　Who are rather small,
Can't seem to learn
　The steps at all.

— *Marchette Chute*

139

140

The Last Blue Whale

George McCue

Ben Blue Whale is alone. Every day he swims
a long way looking for another blue whale.
He looks in all parts of the oceans where whales
live. Sometimes he sees other kinds of whales,
but he never sees a blue whale like himself.

Ben has been looking for another blue whale
since his mother was killed. He was small then,
but he still remembers that horrible day.
Ben and his mother heard the noise of a boat.
But before they could swim away, there was
another noise. It was the noise of a gun.
Men on the boat had killed Ben's mother.
Ben didn't understand what had happened
because he didn't know what men or boats were.
All he knew was that his mother was not
with him anymore.

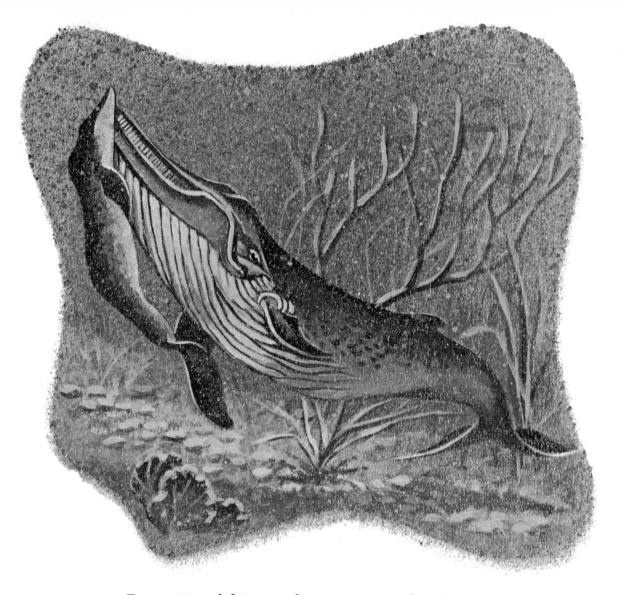

Ben missed his mother very much. She had
taken good care of him since the day he was born.
Like all whales, Ben was born under the water.
As soon as he was born, his mother put her head
under him and helped him to the top of the water
so he could get air. Whales are like people
and other land animals. They must have
air to live.

Ben's mother fed him her milk. He needed
lots of milk every day. It helped him grow
and keep warm. Ben didn't have much hair
to keep him warm, and the ocean water was
very cold. The milk made Ben fat, and the fat
helped him stay warm.

Ben's mother never let other animals hurt him.
Many times hungry killer whales tried to kill Ben.
Sometimes they would bite his mother.
But she didn't care. She would not let them
hurt Ben.

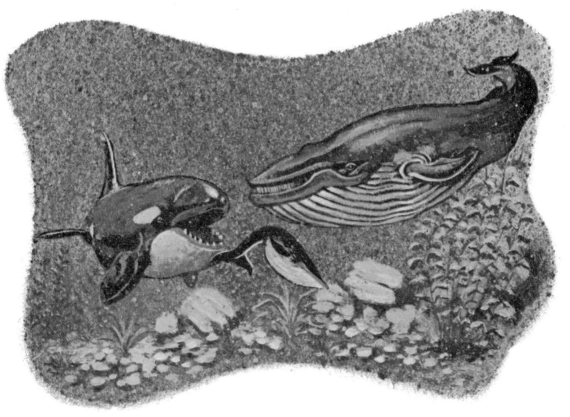

Sometimes Ben's mother sang when she was with him. She didn't sing the way people do. You might not think she sang very well. But Ben loved to hear his mother sing. It told him she was near. And when his mother was near, Ben was safe and happy.

After Ben's mother was gone, Ben was alone in the ocean. But he was lucky. Now he was big, and he could take care of himself. He didn't need his mother's milk anymore. He could eat food that he found in the ocean. To Ben the ocean was like one big bowl of soup.

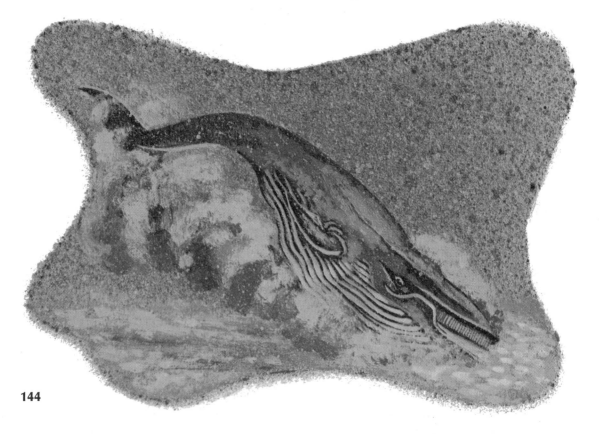

Ben grew and grew until one day he was a big
blue whale. He didn't know it, but he was the
biggest animal in the world. He was 100 feet long.
Since Ben was so big, the killer whales left him
alone. They never tried to hurt him anymore.

Now Ben is older. And he gets more lonely every day. He wants very much to find another blue whale. He wants to have a family. But he never sees another blue whale. Men have killed most of them. Ben is one of the last blue whales left in the world.

Signal Words

Some words are like signals. They tell you that something is coming. The words in red below usually tell you that more words are coming.

The boy went to the museum.

The girl ran down the beach.

The dolphins jumped into the air.

The waves rolled over the land.

The boy looked at the moon.

I found this shell on the beach.

Here are some more signal words. Can you use them in sentences?

up	by	before	above	below
from	with	inside	behind	through

Phrase Markers. Have the paragraph and the sentences below it read. Let the children make up sentences using the prepositions listed. Write their sentences on the board, underlining the prepositional phrases. When all the sentences are on the board, have just the phrases read so the children will get the feeling of a phrase and its function.

A Home in the Desert

Olga Economakis

Abu's home was the desert, all of the desert.
Abu didn't live in a house in one place like
other children but in a tent with his mother
and father. Their tent moved with them. And
their animals moved with them as they looked
for grass and water. Always looking. Never
staying. From place to place in the desert,
they went—every new place just like the last
and no place with even a name.

In summer the sun would dry up
the springs so there was no water for grass
to grow. And as Abu's father put up the tent,
he would say, "Tomorrow we will move on.
We may find grass ahead for the animals."
So just about every day they would pack up
their things and move on to a new place.
Once Abu's father told him a story about
the ocean. "Is the desert like the ocean,
Father?" Abu asked.

"Yes, my child," said his father. "In many ways
the desert is like the ocean. But in place
of water, we have sand."

Abu liked to think of the desert as an ocean.
Riding on his camel he would pretend he was
on a boat looking for an island. An island big
enough and green enough could be called
his home. He could give it a name.

Most of the time Abu was happy. Mornings
he liked to watch the sun come up like a ball
right out of the sand. And at night he liked
to hear the sound of his mother and father
talking outside the tent.

On nights when the sides of the tent were up
to let in the air, Abu would look at the little
stars in the sky. He would pretend that they
were his sheep. He would watch over them
until he fell asleep and his mother came
into the tent to cover him up.

Other times, after a hot day of looking for
a water hole, Abu would pretend that each star
was a drop of water. "If we had that water,"
he said, "we would never have to move again.
Our tent would be a real home. Mother would
not have to keep packing all our things, and
Father would have a real chair to sit on."

But Abu's father just laughed and said,
"When summer comes, the water dries up,
and the grass does not grow. Would you want
your animals to go without water?"
Abu knew then that this was not an island
he could name. It was another too-dry-place.
They would have to pull up the tent poles
and go out into the big desert that he had
to call home.

Oasis of the Stars

One day Abu asked his father if he could dig into the sand to see where the water went.

"I want to try to find my shimmering stars, my little drops of water," Abu said. "If I dig long enough and deep enough, maybe I will find them."

"Dig for stars?" his father laughed. "My child, there is nothing under the sand but more sand. Soon we must move on again."

But Abu asked once more, "Please, Father, may I just try?"

His father smiled. "Well, you may look. But remember when our spring runs dry, we must be on our way."

That very night Abu found a place where the
grass was a little greener than any other place.
And that's where he began to dig.

Night after night he dug. After a while
his hole was deep enough so he could stand
in it up to his knees. But there was no water.

It was hard work. The sand sometimes fell
back into the hole, and Abu had to make
a wall of rocks around it. Under the sand
he found hard-packed earth and rocks.
Sometimes he dug with his hands
around a big rock to pull it out.

Deeper and deeper he went until just
his head could be seen above the hole.
But still there was no water.

Sometimes Abu wanted to give up.
Then he would look up into the night and
always the shimmering stars would be there,
all over the sky, looking like little drops
of water. And always, after seeing them, he
would dig some more. But Abu's water stayed
in the sky. His little hole in the big desert
was now above his head, and there was
no water at all.

Sometimes Abu's father would come and look into the hole. "Abu, have you found them yet, your shimmering stars? Well, never mind. Summer is coming. We will find water in some other place."

Then one day while Abu worked, his father came to him to say that the spring had run dry. They would leave the next morning.

Abu cried that night as he dug deeper into the hole. If only his tears could help. But tears were not enough. They could never fill up a hole so deep. "I will never find stars in the earth," he thought. The stars were in the sky. The earth was only desert.

As Abu climbed to the top of the hole,
he could feel something cool. "The earth
is cool," said Abu. "It feels damp. But it is
only my tears." Then he picked up some dirt
from another part of the hole. "It feels
different," he thought.

"*Father,* please come!" he cried. "The earth
is damp. There must be water under here."

Abu's father was sitting outside the tent.
He didn't get up but smiled and said,
"It feels that way because the night air
makes the earth cool. Come, child, stop
your digging, and sit with me. I will tell
you about the ocean. You like that story."

But Abu went on digging. He couldn't see
out of the hole now. To carry the dirt out
he had to climb up little stairs he had made
in the side of the hole. At last he fell asleep,
and his father had to carry him into the tent.
As he put Abu to bed, he smiled. "The child
has dreams, and sometimes dreams hurt.
But dreams, like water and food, make boys
grow into men."

The next day the camels were packed.
Abu went to take a last look at the hole
he had made. He looked at his rock wall.
Then his eyes went down the stairs
he had made. At last he was looking
at the bottom of the hole. At the bottom
the sand was darker than it had been. He took
off his shoes and started down the stairs.

Deeper and deeper he went until he reached
the bottom of the hole, and his feet could feel
wet sand. He got down on his knees to feel it
with his hands. It was wet. It was really wet!

"Please, Father, come quickly," he cried.
"The water is here. *It's here!*"

Abu's father looked at Abu on his knees
at the bottom of the hole. Then he climbed
into the hole and picked up some sand.
It was wet. "My child, you were right,"
he said. "Your shimmering stars were there
under the sand. We will stay here."

So Abu and his father made the hole
into a well. Now their tent is
a real home with a real chair
for his father. And his mother doesn't have
to keep packing their things.

And now when the sun goes down and night
falls on the desert, Abu looks into his well
and sees his shimmering stars. He has named
the place he lives Oasis of the Stars.

The Waters of the Earth

PHOTOGRAPH, ERICH LESSING, MAGNUM

Noah Releasing the Dove

ARTIST UNKNOWN

Many artists have chosen water as a subject for their work.
One artist showed Noah in the ark. He made the picture
by fitting together bits of brightly colored glass. Such
pictures are called mosaics.

Fishing Boat

INGBET

This is a photograph of a fishing boat resting safely in the harbor after a day at sea. The soft colors help to give us a quiet feeling.

Sailing Ship

HOLDEN WEINTRAUB

A boy in the second grade made this crayon drawing of a sailing ship. Crayon drawings may be seen in many fine museums.

COLLECTION, WHITNEY MUSEUM OF AMERICAN ART, NEW YORK

Venice

LOREN MacIVER

Here are three different views of Venice, an old seaport, famous for its beautiful harbor and canals. One shows a city of bright colors and interesting shapes. Another is a lifelike painting of the Grand Canal. A third is a woodcut of the harbor.

FOTO CINE BRUNEL, LUGANO; THYSSEN BORNEMISZA COLLECTION, SWITZERLAND   COURTESY, THE HAMLYN GROUP

THE CLEVELAND MUSEUM OF ART—
PURCHASE FROM THE J. H. WADE FUND

The Grand Canal

CANALETTO

Bird's-eye View of Venice

JACOPO DE' BARBARI

Toilers of the Sea

ALBERT PINKHAM RYDER

In this painting the fishermen's boat seems to be part of
the sea. It glides along beneath a partly darkened sky, the
sun lighting its way.

PHILLIPS ACADEMY, ANDOVER, MASSACHUSETTS

Amida, or Buddha Falls, Kiso

KATSUSHIKA HOKUSAI

The artist who made this woodcut of a waterfall didn't
try to make it look real. He showed us a beautiful
arrangement of shapes and colors.

PHILADELPHIA MUSEUM OF ART: THE SAMUEL S. WHITE III AND VERA WHITE COLLECTION

COLLECTION OF THE UNIVERSITY OF MICHIGAN MUSEUM OF ART

Sea and Rain

JAMES McNEILL WHISTLER

In this painting the artist used bands of soft colors. The blue-green sea gives us the peaceful feeling of walking alone on a rainy day.

Way
Down
Deep

Underneath the water
Way down deep
In sand and stones and seaweed
Starfish creep
Snails inch slowly
Oysters sleep
Underneath the water
Way down deep.

—Mary Ann Hoberman

The Sky Above

February Twilight

I stood beside a hill
   Smooth with new-laid snow,
A single star looked out
   From the cold evening glow.

There was no other creature
   That saw what I could see—
I stood and watched the evening star
   As long as it watched me.

—Sara Teasdale

171

Barbara Brenner

The Flying Patchwork Quilt

If it weren't for my mother, it would never
have happened. You see, my mother collects
things and keeps the stuff around the house.

One day my mother came home with an old
chest. "It will be a great place to store winter
clothes," she told my father. "And look what's
at the bottom of it."

"What is it?" asked my father. He doesn't
like old stuff the way my mother does.

"It's an old patchwork quilt," Mother said.
"Isn't it beautiful?"

"It's nice," my father said, "but what are
you going to do with it?"

"It'll come in handy," my mother said.
That's what my mother always says when she
doesn't know what to do with one of her old
things. She folded the quilt and put it away
in the chest.

That was the last I saw of the patchwork quilt for a long time. It lay at the bottom of the old chest, and when spring came it got covered with winter clothes.

Then one day I saw the quilt again. It was all because of my sister Ellen. Ellen is only five, and she's always going through a stage. Then she was going through the stage where she wanted to fly. She was always trying. She tried everything. I told her it wouldn't work, but she went on trying.

Well, one day Ellen and I were outside when my mother came out. "Carl," she said to me. "I have to go to the store. Will you keep an eye on Ellen?"

"Sure," I said. "Don't worry about a thing." So my mother went off down the street.

I was working on a rabbit house, so I was really keeping more of an ear on Ellen than an eye on her. She talks to herself. I thought that as long as I could hear her talking, she was all right.

She started to play her flying game. She was standing on the stairs with a balloon tied around her. I watched her jump and land right on the balloon. It broke with a pop!

I began to feel a little sorry for her. "Ellen," I called to her, "it won't work. You have to wave your arms if you're going to fly."

"It will so work," Ellen said. "I just haven't found the right flying thing yet. You'll see." And with that, she ran off into the apartment.

A few minutes after that I looked up and there was Ellen. She was about to try flying with the old patchwork quilt. "No, you don't," I yelled. "That's Mother's."

"Please, Carl. Just this once. I'll put it right back," she said. "I just want to try it."

"All right," I said. "But promise that after you fall with the silly thing you will stop playing this game for the rest of the afternoon!"

She promised. I helped her pin it on, and I gave
her a hand up onto the stairs again. "Don't forget
to wave your arms," I said.

Ellen yelled,
"One,

two,

three."

"Jump," I said.

She did. Now, I'm not making this up. One
minute she was jumping off the stairs. And
the next minute she was floating over my head.
Flying! Laughing and flying all over the place.

"I told you, I told you!" she yelled. *"I knew
the patchwork quilt was the right thing."*

I just stood there with my mouth open. A
little wind came along, and she floated up
higher. She began to look a little afraid.

"Carl?" she called, kind of funny.
I reached for her leg and missed.

The wind took Ellen higher and higher and
before I knew it, she was flying over the treetops.

"Don't worry. I'm coming," I yelled as I ran
down the street after her. I stopped when I
got to the corner, but there was no sign of her.
Everything was just the way it always is
at the corner.

Mr. Peters was sitting next to his newspaper
stand. "Mr. Peters, Mr. Peters," I said.
"Did you see my sister fly by just now?"

"In a balloon or a jet?" Mr. Peters laughed.

I didn't think that was very funny. "It was
a patchwork . . . Oh, never mind," I said.

"Sorry, Carl, I haven't seen her," said
Mr. Peters. "But if she lands around here,
I'll let you know," he called after me as I left.

The Missing Quilt

I ran up and down the streets, trying
to look up at the sky at the same time. It wasn't
until I got to the library that I saw Ellen.
She was caught on top of the library flagpole.
Boy, was I happy to see her!

I ran into the library to get someone
to help me. **"Mrs. Bright,"** I called.

Mrs. Bright hurried over. "Shhhhhhhh," she said.

*"But Mrs. Bright, my sister is
outside on the flagpole, and . . ."*

"Well, tell her to get off, dear. We don't like
children climbing on the flagpole."

"You don't understand!"

"Shhhhhhhh."

*"I can't help it. My sister
needs help now!"*

"Whatever are you talking about, Carl?"

*"My sister has been flying all over the city,
and now she's caught on top of the flagpole."*

"What!
Carl, are you making this up?"

I looked her right in the eye and said,
"No, Mrs. Bright. And please hurry."

We ran out of the library and looked up at the top
of the flagpole. But Ellen was not there.

I looked at Mrs. Bright, and she looked at me.
What could I say? She'd never believe me now.
So I just walked away.

"Well, let's face it," I said to myself. "Your sister is gone, and no one will help you because no one will believe you."

I thought about going to the police and saying, "You see, my sister flew away. She was wearing a patchwork quilt." What a horrible thought!

I walked back to the apartment. I really
didn't want to face my mother, but I knew
I had to. Mother was getting lunch just
as if nothing had happened.

"Mother," I said, "something horrible
has happened."

"What?" asked my mother. "Where?"

"Right here. But I couldn't help it,"
I said.

"I'm sure you couldn't," said my mother.
"But tell me about it."

"It's Ellen," I began.

"Yes," Mother said. "I told you to keep an eye on her, but when I came home you were gone."

"I tried to watch her, but I couldn't keep up with her," I said.

Mother smiled. How could she at a time like this?

"Now, come on, Carl. She's been standing there by that tree ever since I left," Mother said.

"What tree? Where?" I asked.

I ran to the window. I could hardly believe my eyes. But sure enough, there was Ellen. She was standing by the tree, talking to herself.

I ran out to her, trying to keep myself from doing something silly like kissing her. "*Where have you been?*" I yelled, acting very mad.

"I remembered what you said about waving my arms," Ellen said. "So I did, and all at once I was here. And now I'm caught on this tree, and I can't get the quilt off. I don't want to tear it because Mother will be mad. Will you help me, Carl?"

Now that Ellen was safe, I started to think about what had happened that morning. Someone could *fly* with that quilt on!

I thought about pinning the quilt on myself and flying to see my grandmother at the beach or my uncle at the farm. But my flying dreams were ended by my sister.

"Carl, please help me," she said.

While I was helping her, I said, "Now, remember, not a word about this to Mother. She doesn't even know we have the quilt. I'll put it back in the chest."

I got it into the apartment without Mother seeing it. But as I was putting it in the chest, I thought, "Why wait? Why not take a ride tonight?" So I put the quilt in my room.

That night I had everything set for the takeoff. When everyone was in bed, I opened the window. I looked up into the dark sky. There was a moon. That would help. I picked up the quilt to pin it on.

"Well, here goes!" I said. Then I dropped the pin. I put the quilt down to get another pin, and then it happened. The wind caught the quilt, and it went flying out the window. I reached for it, but I missed it. In two minutes it was out of sight.

We never saw the patchwork quilt again.
I'd think I dreamed it all if it weren't
for Ellen. She remembers everything. Mother
remembers, too, in a way. Every once
in a while she says, "I wonder what became
of that lovely quilt that was in the chest?"

Then my sister gives me that look as if
to say, "Why don't we tell her?"

But I don't want to. No one would believe us.

Ellen's out of her flying stage now. But I
still think about flying a lot.

One day my mother came home with an old rug.
It looked just like any other rug. But if someone
were to take that rug to the top of the stairs
and sit in the middle of it . . .

Well, who knows?

I Can Fly

I can fly, of course,
Very low,
Not fast,
Rather slow.
I spread my arms
Like wings,
Lean on the wind,
And my body zings
About.
Nothing showy—
A few loops
And turns—
But for the most
Part,
I just coast.
However,
Since people are prone
To talk about
It,
I generally prefer,
Unless I am alone,
Just to walk about.

—Felice Holman

Dina Anastasio

The Race

On the morning of Pete's first race, Jenny took the stairs to the roof two at a time. When she pulled open the door and ran outside, she was a little sad. She wasn't sure that she wanted the race to take place after all.

The night before, Jenny had taken her pigeon to the place where the race would begin. When she left him, she was very happy. She couldn't wait for morning when the race would start. Now she was surprised that she wasn't happy anymore. Jenny was afraid.

Jenny had spent many days teaching her pigeon to find his way home from far away. She knew that he did it very well. But she knew that sometimes things happened to pigeons as they flew home. And once in a while they didn't come back at all.

"It's Pete's first race," she thought. "Anything could happen. But I'm just being silly," she told herself. "Pete's big and fast. He's been far away before, and he's always come back."

Most of the time Pete was back home before Jenny was. But this time things were different. This was a race. Jenny didn't know if Pete was as fast as the other birds or if he could win a race.

Jenny sat on the roof and tried to picture what Pete was doing. Soon someone would open his cage and let him fly out into the bright sky.

At ten Jenny heard the telephone ring. Then her mother climbed up to the roof to tell her that Pete had been set free. He had started the long trip home.

As the morning grew hotter and hotter, Jenny sat quietly on the roof. She watched the ant-like people on the street below. But today the people below couldn't take her mind off Pete. And every few minutes she looked at the sky to see if she could see him.

When the noon whistle sounded, Jenny became afraid. Pete had never taken this long to fly this far before. She knew that something must have happened.

When her mother came up to the roof to tell her that lunch was ready, Jenny looked out at the clear summer sky. "He's never coming back, is he, Mother?" she asked.

"He's always come back before," her mother said. "I'm sure he'll be back soon. Pigeons can fly in rain and snow or when they're sick or hungry. That's why pigeons carried messages in the war."

"*Messages?*" asked Jenny. "How did they do that?"

"The messages were tied to their legs," said Jenny's mother. "They flew the messages from the battlefields back to headquarters. Sometimes they were days late, but most of them made it. And so will Pete."

Jenny was not so sure. "What if Pete missed our roof and landed on a different one? Or what if he ran into something and was too badly hurt to fly all the way home?" she thought.

Jenny knew that it was too late for Pete to win the race. But she didn't care about that now. She just wanted him back.

"I don't think I'll have any lunch," she told her mother. And she turned back to watch the sky. When she saw no sign of Pete, she looked down at the noontime street below.

Jenny's mother went downstairs. In a few minutes she came back with a small chair and two sandwiches. She placed them beside Jenny and went back down to their small apartment.

After a while she went up to the roof again. Jenny was still sitting in the chair, and the sandwiches were just where she had put them. So she carried them back downstairs and left Jenny alone to wait for Pete.

The Long Wait

When Jenny's father came home, Jenny was still on the roof. The sky was getting dark.

"Pete didn't come home," Jenny said quietly when she heard her father behind her.

"I know," he said as he sat down beside her. To take her mind off Pete, he began to tell her a story. It was about some brave pigeons that carried messages in the war.

But Jenny didn't care about other pigeons. She cared only about Pete. Was he lost? Was he hungry? Could he find his way home in the dark?

As Jenny's father told his story, the sky
became darker and darker. Jenny moved closer
to her father. She felt so sad that soon
she began to cry.

"I guess you don't care much about other birds
when Pete is lost, do you?" her father asked.
"I'm sorry. I should have told you another
kind of story. Would you like it if I just
sat here with you? We don't have to talk at all
if you don't want to."

So Jenny's father stayed there with her on the
roof. And together they waited for Pete.

Jenny was watching the street below light up for the night when she heard her father say, "*Jenny, Jenny, look!*" Quickly he pulled her to her feet and showed her a small dot in the sky.

Carefully they watched as the dot moved closer and closer until at last they were sure. *It was Pete! He wasn't lost after all.*

Jenny ran to the other side of the roof to wait for Pete to land. He was flying very slowly, and Jenny was afraid he was hurt. At last he flew close enough for Jenny to reach him. She took him in her arms and carried him over to the light. She felt his legs and looked at him carefully until she was sure that he was not hurt.

"*He came back, he came back,*" she said over and over to her father. Then she got Pete some food and water, and she put him carefully into his box.

"Where did you go?" she asked as she closed the top of the box. "What happened to you?"

But Jenny felt sure that she would never know what had happened to Pete. And she really didn't care now that he was home.

More Signal Words

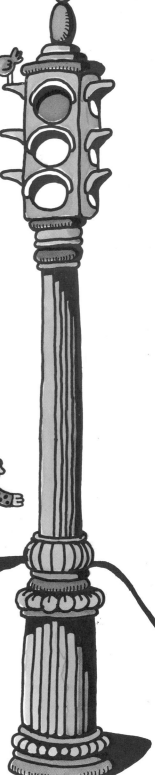

The words in red are signal words. They tell you that more words are coming to add information to the sentence.

Butch was sad as he walked home.
Ben could eat the food that he found.
Jenny looked up when she heard her father.
We were quiet while the band played.
I haven't seen her since we got here.
We ran until we got home.

Here are some more signal words. Can you use them in sentences?

because **whose** **wherever** **whenever**

Clause Markers. Have the paragraphs and sentences read. Let the children make up sentences using the signal words above.

The Mystery

Stanley E. Loeb

It wasn't that Tommy didn't want to go to the country. He just wasn't as happy as everyone seemed to think he should be.

He had only met Aunt Sally and Uncle Harry once. They had come to the city, and they hadn't been much fun. First of all, they couldn't find the apartment. And when they got there at last, they couldn't find a place to park their car.

When they all went out to eat, Aunt Sally and Uncle Harry kept saying that food cost too much in the city. They seemed to think that everything in the country was better.

Tommy had never been to the country, but he knew deep down that he liked the city better. If Aunt Sally and Uncle Harry were what country people were like, he'd keep his friends in the city.

Tommy's mother, on the other hand, was acting as if this trip to the country was the biggest thing in the world. "It's going to be wonderful for you to be in the clean air for the summer," she kept saying.

Tommy knew that city air was not too clean. The newspapers had stories about that. And they kept talking about it on the radio and TV. But leaving your friends all summer just because of a little dirt—that Tommy couldn't see.

"There are a lot of mysteries in the country that you don't know about," said Tommy's mother. "There's more to the country than clean air."

"What do you mean?" asked Tommy.

"You'll find out," said Tommy's mother.

Tommy had been in the country for a few days, and he hadn't found any mysteries yet. The air was clean, and the grass was green. But Tommy missed his friends. He missed the streets and the noise. And he even missed the dirt a little.

Today Tommy had gone fishing with Uncle Harry. They rowed way out on the lake in Uncle Harry's rowboat. Tommy rowed part of the way. He knew how because they have rowboats in the park in the city.

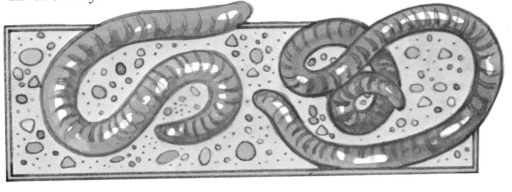

The fishing trip would have been great. But Tommy didn't like putting worms on the hooks. It wasn't that he was afraid. He just didn't like to hold worms, that's all. Besides, there wasn't any mystery about worms anyhow. There were worms in the park in the city. Tommy didn't like city worms any better than country worms. He felt better when they rowed home again.

Tommy still hadn't found the mysteries his mother had promised him. So that night Tommy went to Uncle Harry. "Mother told me there were mysteries in the country," he said. "But I haven't found any."

"There's a mystery outside," said Uncle Harry. "Want to come with me and see?"

"Sure," said Tommy. "But I hope the mystery doesn't turn out to be where worms go at night," he thought.

The Giant in the Sky

Outside the night was still and cool and very
quiet. As Tommy and Uncle Harry walked away
from the house, the sky seemed to get brighter.

"It's not as dark as I thought it was,"
said Tommy.

"Your eyes are getting used to the night,"
said Uncle Harry. "This is a special night. Can
you find the moon?"

Tommy thought the moon would be really big.
It always looked big when they showed it on TV.

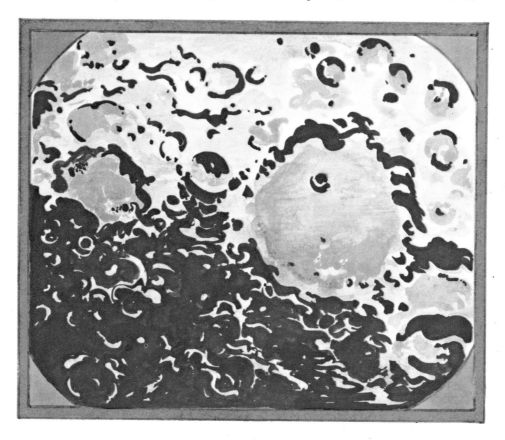

But when he looked up all he could see was stars.
"I can't find the moon," said Tommy.

"It's there," said Uncle Harry. "Just look."

"It's not there," said Tommy. "Oh, wait. There
it is. But it looks so small."

"The moon is very small now," said Uncle Harry.
"But it will be big and bright in a few days.
That's why tonight is special. When the moon is
small like this, you can see lots of stars.
A bright moon hides lots of little stars."

"I don't know anything about stars," said Tommy.
"Are they bright like that all the time?"

"They are," said Uncle Harry. "But you can see
them only when it is dark. That's why a big
bright moon covers up the little stars. The stars
are bright in the daytime, but the sunlight hides
almost all of them. The sun even hides the moon
most of the time. But the sun is a star."

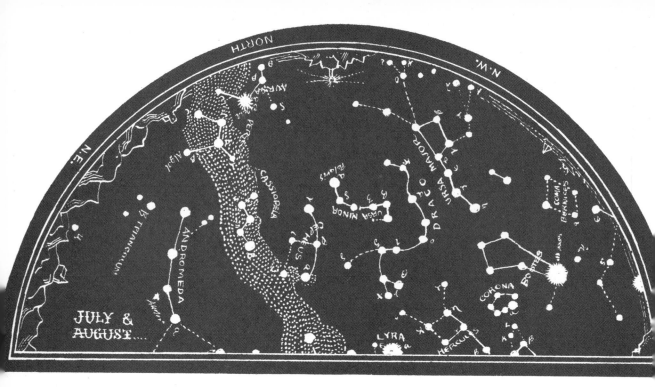

"*The sun is a star!*" said Tommy, surprised.

"Oh, yes, it's a star," said Uncle Harry. "It looks so big because it's the only star near the earth. It's so hot that it heats the earth and the moon, too."

"How do you know all that?" asked Tommy.

"Well," said Uncle Harry, "here in the country, I think a lot about the stars. I read books about them, too. And I come here and watch the stars more than your Aunt Sally likes."

"You do?" said Tommy.

"Men have always thought about the stars,"
said Uncle Harry very quietly. "Long ago men
looked at the stars to tell which way
they were going."

"How did they know which stars to look at?"
asked Tommy. "They look alike
to me. And there are so many of them."

"You're not used to looking at them,"
said Uncle Harry. "Do you see that bright star
over there? That's the North Star. If you walk
toward it, you will be walking north. A man who
wants to go north in a boat just heads his boat
toward the North Star."

"That's something!" said Tommy.

"Right," said Uncle Harry. "Men have looked
at the stars for so many years that they have
picked out lots of them. If you look from the
North Star to the middle of the sky, you can
see three bright stars close together. There, do
you see them?"

"Now I can't find the North Star. Which one
was it? Oh, there it is again. Now where do
I look to find the three stars?" asked Tommy.

"From the North Star to the middle of the sky,"
said Uncle Harry.

"Wait, there, I see them. I see them!"
said Tommy.

"That's Orion's belt. Orion is a giant man.
Look above the three stars in Orion's belt, and
you can see his head. Look down, and you can
see Orion's legs," said Uncle Harry.

"Someone must have looked at the sky for a long
time to see a man and a belt," said Tommy.

"Yes," said Uncle Harry. "Remember, men were looking at the stars long before they were living in cities. They have seen lots of things in the sky."

"Are there other men in the sky besides Orion?" asked Tommy.

"Oh, yes," said Uncle Harry. "But there are other things, too. There are animals and pots and pans and all kinds of things."

"Do you know how to find them all?" asked Tommy.

"Most of them," said Uncle Harry. "But there's always something new. And that's why the stars are a mystery. We can see them, night after night, but we still know very little about them."

Tommy and Uncle Harry kept looking at the stars. It was very late when they started back toward the house.

From then on Tommy and Uncle Harry went out to look at the stars almost every night. Every night the sky looked different.

Tommy thought about the city. In the city you couldn't ever really see the stars. The air was too full of dirt, and the lights were too bright.

When the summer was over, Tommy was happy to be going back to his friends in the city. He just wasn't as happy as he thought he'd be.

In the Country

I think people wonder
in the country much more
than they wonder in the city
with houses next door:

They see more world
in the country, more sky,
so there's much more space
for wondering. That's why!

— Aileen Fisher

Same Sound–Different Letters

Sometimes different letters stand for the same sound. All the words in each box below have the same vowel sound. But each of them is spelled with different letters.

sea	mystery
free	pin
believe	build
he	busy
any	been

lake	kept
day	friend
rain	said
they	head
eight	any

Phoneme-Grapheme Relationships. Have the sentences and the words in each box read. Point out the vowel sound and the letters that represent it in each box.

Walker, the Witch, and the Striped Flying Saucer

*"Would you like to hear about
me and the flying saucer,
Alberta?" asked Walker.*

"Sure," answered Alberta.

*"If I told you, you
might not believe me,"
said Walker.*

"Maybe I would," said Alberta.

*"Well," said Walker. "It all
started one night when a
witch flew by my window.
Do you believe it so far,
Alberta?"*

"I think so," answered Alberta.

"Hello, Walker," yelled the witch. "Have you seen that flying saucer tonight?"

"Which flying saucer?" I said.

"The big one with the stripes," she yelled as she flew away. "Just like your pajamas."

I couldn't believe that a flying saucer could have the same stripes as my pajamas, so I went out to take a look around.

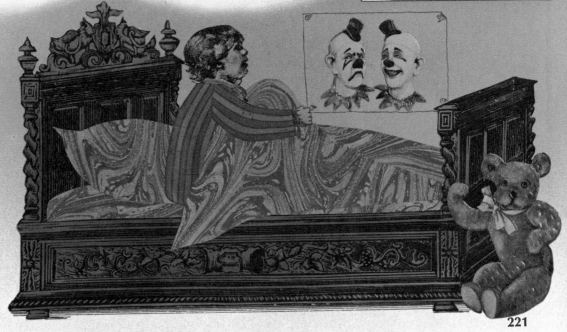

As I looked around a big tree, I saw a great big flying saucer with stripes like my pajamas. A man wearing a striped hat came out of the saucer and waved to me.

"Come on up," he called.

"How?" I yelled.

"Get into the balloon. I'll pull you up," he said.

I got into the balloon and the man pulled me up to the saucer.

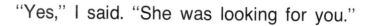

"You haven't seen an old witch flying around, have you?" he asked me as I got out of the balloon.

"Yes," I said. "She was looking for you."

"Hm-m," he said. "That old witch is bad news."

He gave me some cookies and milk and went on talking about the witch.

"The witch doesn't like to have anyone flying around who isn't a witch."

"How can she stop you?" I asked.

"Who knows?" he answered. "The last time she flew over the saucer, she said she would make me disappear. But this is too nice a night to worry about that old witch."

"Say," the man said,
"do you like to fly airplanes?"

"I don't mind," I said.

"I have this airplane I'd like you
to try," he said. "Just push the button
that says Go, and you'll go."

I got into the airplane, pushed the Go button,
and went up in the sky. Way down below I could
see the flying saucer and the man waving.

"Nice flying!" called the man as I came
in for a fast landing.

"Want to try the jet next?"

"Sure," I said.

I climbed up into the jet, sat down, and pushed the Go button. That jet was great. I made loop-the-loops and dives and everything. I flew around for a long time, and I went all over the sky.

But when I flew back to where the flying saucer had been, it was gone. I landed the jet and got out. The old witch was standing in the field.

"Where's the flying saucer?" I asked.

"I made it disappear," she answered. "And now I'm going to make that airplane you were in disappear, too!"

The witch turned to the jet, waved her arms, yelled something I didn't understand, and the jet disappeared. This made the witch very happy, and she started laughing and jumping all around.

I was so mad, I turned to the witch and yelled the same thing she had said a minute ago. And to my surprise the witch disappeared. There was nothing but grass where she had been.

I started to go home. I was feeling sad. I thought maybe the flying saucer and the nice man and everything had been a dream.

But then I had a big surprise. Right in the middle of the field, I found a striped hat. So I knew it had been real.

As I picked up the hat, I felt something fly just over my head. I couldn't see it, but I heard a voice say, "Good-by, Walker. I'll be back some day."

I waved good-by and went home to bed.

"Well, Alberta," said Walker,
"did you believe my story?"

"Most of it," said Alberta.

"Well, some parts were more
real than others," said Walker.
"But that's the way I remember it."

"I believed a lot of it," said Alberta.

Hurricanes and Birthday Cake

A REAL STORY BY ELIZABETH LEVY WITH PICTURES TAKEN BY HER FAMILY

Whenever my family gets together — uncles, aunts, and cousins — they all talk about the time that Liz ate the birthday cake in the middle of a hurricane. Then everyone laughs, and I do, too. Only I can't remember the hurricane or the cake because I was only two years old.

I wish I could remember. It makes me a little sad that I can't. From what everyone tells me, that was an exciting day, the day I ate the birthday cake. It was the most exciting day of my life, and I don't even remember it.

The hurricane came at the end of a summer during World War Two. My uncle was a doctor, and he worked in a hospital by the ocean. He took care of the men who got hurt on the battlefields of Europe.

My father was fighting in the war. He had
seen me only once when I was just a few days old.
Since then he had been away fighting, but I was
really too little to miss him.

Anyway the summer I was two, my aunt
and uncle asked my mother to bring my brother
and me and come visit them. We lived far from
the ocean, where it was very hot in the summer.
My mother was really happy to take a trip
to the ocean. My brother was happy, too,
because he liked to visit my two cousins.

My aunt and uncle had a house right by the ocean, so we spent most of our summer on the beach. My mother has pictures of all of us swimming and playing in the sand. Even now I think the ocean is scary, so I must have thought so then, too. My mother says even my brother was afraid of the ocean at first.

During the summer my mother and aunt helped out at the hospital. My grandmother took care of my brother and my cousins and me most of the time. I guess taking care of us was a lot of work, but my grandmother says that she had fun doing it. She says she misses the time when we were all little.

Soon it was the end of the summer and the end of our visit. We had to get back home because school was starting. We really should have left before. But my mother's birthday was coming up, and my aunt and uncle wanted to be with her on her birthday. I think they were afraid that she might be lonely without my father.

The day before my mother's birthday, we heard about a hurricane. Or I guess my family started to hear about a hurricane. I was too little to understand.

Hurricanes are one of the most horrible kinds of storms there can be. Sometimes the winds go as fast as the fastest cars. The hurricane winds can make houses fall down. They can make the ocean come up on land. Then there are floods.

THIS IS HOW A HURRICANE LOOKS FROM OUTER SPACE.

You just can't tell which way a hurricane will move. That's why they give hurricanes girls' names like Amy, Ellen, Jenny, or Marie. They say you can never be sure just what a hurricane is going to do next, just as you can't tell what a girl will do next.

Whenever a hurricane heads for land, there's trouble. This summer it looked as if the hurricane was heading right for us. All the men in the town started filling bags with sand. They put the sandbags around the houses. The sandbags would help the houses stand up when the winds came.

That night, my aunt and uncle and my mother talked about leaving the house. But they thought they'd be safe with the sandbags all around the house.

My aunt went ahead and made the cake for my mother's birthday party. But during the morning of my mother's birthday, the hurricane really hit. It was very exciting at first. Then the house started to shake. The rain came down harder than anyone had ever seen.

My cousins were so afraid, they started to cry.
My brother cried, too. My mother tried to keep
them quiet, but she was afraid. Everyone knew
that we had to get out of the house, because if
the ocean came up, we might all be killed in the
floods. But the wind was so bad that if we went
outside, we might be killed by the wind.

It must have been horrible, but I was too little to know about the trouble we were in. Everyone was running around. And there in the middle of the table sat the birthday cake.

No one was watching me. Somehow I climbed on a chair. Then I climbed on top of the table. And in the middle of the hurricane, I sat on the table and had a big birthday cake all to myself.

I was eating away happily when the police came. They had come to take us to a safe place.

My mother and aunt were so happy to see the police, they almost cried. Before the police came, they were really afraid we would all be killed. They started to get everyone together, and that's when they noticed me.

There I was, sitting in the middle of the table with birthday cake all over me. While everyone was worrying about the trouble we were in, I had had a good time. There was cake all over my face, on my clothes, and even in my hair.

It made everyone laugh. My mother says that just seeing me made her feel brave.

Two policemen carried my grandmother,
because she was so old. Another policeman
carried me, and we all made it out safely.

Later the floods came and ruined the house.
If the police hadn't come when they did, we might
never have gotten out of there.

So that's the story of the day I ate the birthday
cake. Everyone in my family tells me it really
happened just like that, but I can't be sure. I
was only two, and I don't remember
the hurricane at all.

Ramu and the Kite

MEHLLI GOBHAI

Ramu was eight the year his father gave him two rupees for his very first kite. With the two rupees in his hand, Ramu ran to a little store filled with kites.

After much thought Ramu bought a blue fighter kite with a bright red tail. It cost one rupee. With the other rupee Ramu bought the string and a holder to wind the string on. The string was a special kind that was coated with small bits of glass. Because of the glass, the string could be used to cut down another kite.

Ramu gave his two rupees to the man in the kite store and ran home to show his father the kite he had bought.

That night Ramu's father showed him how to string a kite. The boy watched as his father made holes in the paper with a small stick. Then he put the string through the holes and made a knot.

When the kite was ready, Ramu put it in a safe place in his room. It was still eight days until Kite Day. And no boy would think of flying his kite before that day.

On the morning of Kite Day, Ramu watched the older boys start out for the park with their kites. He knew he was not ready to go with them. So Ramu's father took the boy to the little field behind their house to teach him to fly a kite.

Ramu's father held the string while Ramu walked a few yards away from him with the kite. Ramu's father said, "Now!" And Ramu jumped into the air, pushing the kite as far up as he could reach. For a minute, kite and boy were in the air. Then the boy landed on the grass, and the kite headed up into the sky.

Now Ramu's father put the string into Ramu's hand. The boy was alone with his kite. The rest of the world seemed far, far away.

Soon Ramu's kite was so far up in
the sky, he could hardly see it. The string
felt tight. Then all at once the kite
started to fall towards the earth.
Ramu heard his father call, "Pull!"

Ramu pulled quickly on the string.
Almost at once the kite righted itself
and floated up into the open sky.

To Ramu it seemed only a few minutes
before his father called, "Time to go home."
Ramu started to pull the kite in. The
kite seemed to be fighting every bit
of the way. At last the boy held it in his
arms again. And yet, it wouldn't be still.
It was like a bird that wanted to be free.

Ramu took the kite to the field behind
his house every day. After eight days he
knew he was ready to fly his kite with
the other boys.

The Silver Kite

When Ramu reached the park in the morning, the sky was already full of kites. Ramu started to fly his. The blue kite did just what Ramu wanted it to, and soon it was floating along in the wind with the other kites.

All at once a big red kite was heading towards Ramu's kite. Ramu pulled at the string. The blue kite climbed quickly up into the sky. Ramu's kite just missed being cut down by the red kite. From now on Ramu would have to watch carefully and keep an eye on all the kites.

Then Ramu saw the red kite floating
away from the others. Ramu pulled the
string of his kite and it went charging
into battle. Soon the sharp strings
of the two kites were wound around each other.
Each boy was fighting to cut the string
of the other boy's kite. All at once
Ramu saw that the red kite had broken away
and was floating free in the sky. Ramu
had won his first battle!

Some boys began running after the red
kite. They had long branches in their hands.
Ramu watched as a boy caught the kite with one
of the branches. When he got the kite, he ran
off with it.

Ramu looked up to see if his kite was safe. Out of nowhere, it seemed, came a white kite.

Before Ramu could make a move, the string of his kite was wound around the sharp string of the white kite. But this time Ramu was not ready. He pulled on the string, but there was no hope. Ramu saw his kite float off. The string was cut.

The wind pushed the kite into the branches of a tall tree. Even then the blue kite tried to get away. But at last the kite moved no more. It lay still. Ramu saw that the blue paper was ruined. He knew that in a few days there would be nothing left of his beautiful kite.

Ramu walked slowly home. When his mother saw him, she guessed what had happened and left him alone.

That night Ramu told his father the story. "I will give you another rupee to get a new kite," his father said.

"I will never fly another kite," said Ramu.

Ramu lay in his bed that night watching
the moon floating in the sky like a great
silver kite. At last he fell asleep.
While he was sleeping he had a dream.

There was a bright light at the window,
and before Ramu was a kite. It was
silver like the moon. And it was two
times as big as Ramu. It seemed to be
calling to him without words.

Ramu opened the window, and the next
thing he knew, he was holding on
to the silver kite. They were flying through
the air with a sound like the wind
in a forest. Up and up the kite took Ramu
until he could look down on all the roofs
of the town. Soon he was above the clouds,
and he could hardly see the lights
below him.

The kite seemed to be telling Ramu
many things—things he could not really
understand. "I am all kites," it seemed
to say. "I am your blue kite and the red
kite and the white kite. I am all the kites
you will ever fly. I am even the
kite you will dream of but never own."

Ramu and the kite were flying right
at the moon. It came closer and closer
until Ramu couldn't look any longer.
With a sharp cry, he was awake.

It was morning already. The sky was
blue. Near Ramu lay a silver rupee,
as round and bright as the full moon.

Why the Sun Was Late

Benjamin Elkin

It was a quiet afternoon. In the forest there
was a tree that was so old, a small breeze
would make it fall. But the air was still,
and there was no breeze. Only the sound
of a buzzing fly could be heard.

While the tree was waiting for a breeze,
the fly stopped to rest on one of its leaves.
That was all the old tree needed. It fell
over with a crash.

"Buzz!" said the surprised fly. "Who would
have thought that a little fly like me could
knock down a tree?" It was so proud
of itself, it flew away to see what else it
could do.

The fly flew across to the other side
of the forest. It stopped when it saw two boys
climbing a tree to gather nuts. "Here's where
I have some fun," thought the fly. "Won't
those boys be surprised when I knock them
out of the tree!"

The fly buzzed from one boy to the other
trying to make them fall. But the fly wasn't
as mighty as it thought. All it could do was
fly around tickling the boys.

The boys tried to stop the fly from tickling them. One boy began waving his arms, trying to hit the fly. He did not hit the fly, but he did hit something else. He hit the branch he was sitting on. That really started something!

It so happened that three squirrels had been sitting on the same branch as the boys. The squirrels fell down on top of four snakes who were sleeping in the grass.

The four snakes were so scared, they went off into the grass without looking. They ran into five elephants. The elephants were so scared, they began to charge across the field. Crash! The elephants ran headfirst into a hill. They hit the hill so hard that a nest and six eggs fell out of one of the trees.

When the mother bird saw what had happened
to her nest and her eggs, she began to cry.
"Oh, my babies," she cried. "Their shells
are broken. Now my heart is broken, too.
Never, never, **never** will I sing again."

All that afternoon and all that night the
mother bird was quiet. At last it was time
for the sun to come up. But the bird did not
sing her morning wake-up song. Now everyone
knows it's the song of a bird that wakes the
sun. Without that song, the sun went sleeping
on and on. And the day was as dark as night.

The animals waited and waited for the sun
to come up. But not one ray of light did they
see. At last they cried out to the Great Spirit.
The Great Spirit heard the animals and called
them all together.

"Tell me, oh bird," said the Great Spirit.
"Why did you not sing and wake the sun?"

"My heart is broken. I will never sing again.
My six lovely eggs were broken by those five
elephants who came charging across the field,"
said the bird.

"It was not our fault," said the elephants.
"We did not mean to crash into the hill.
All five of us were scared by those
four snakes that came by."

"It was not our fault," said the four snakes.
"We were sleeping, when all at once
three squirrels landed right on top of us."

"We could not help it," said the squirrels.
"The three of us were knocked off our branch
by those two boys."

"It was not our fault," said the boys. "We
were gathering nuts in the tree when this
fly started tickling us."

"Let me see if I have the story right,"
said the Great Spirit.

"The **6** eggs . . .
were broken by the **5** elephants . . .
who were scared by the **4** snakes . . .
who were scared by the **3** squirrels . . .
who were knocked off the branch
by the **2** boys . . .
who were buzzed at by **1** fly.

"So it seems to have started with you, oh fly.
Tell me. Why did you buzz at the two boys?"

The fly did not know what to say. How could
he tell everyone that he thought he had knocked
down a tree all by himself? So all he said
was, "Buzz,
    buzz,
    buzz."

"Come, come," said the Great Spirit. "Tell me why you buzzed at the boys."

"Buzz,
   buzz,
   buzz," said the fly.

"I will give you one more minute to tell me," said the Great Spirit.

"Buzz,
   buzz,
   buzz," said the fly. And not one more word would it say.

"So be it," said the Great Spirit. "You would not tell me when I asked you. So you will never say another word. From now on you will not say anything else but buzz,
                    buzz,
                    buzz."

Then the Great Spirit smiled at the mother
bird and said, "There is no need for your
heart to be broken anymore. Go back to your
nest. You will find that your eggs are all
right again. Now, my child, sing and wake
the sun."

"Oh, thank you," said the mother bird. She
sang a beautiful wake-up song. Slowly, slowly
the sky became bright, and the sun got up
at last. The mother bird returned to the hill
and found her six eggs safely back in the nest.

The five elephants returned to their own place
in the field.

The four snakes went back to sleep
in the grass.

The three squirrels went back to their
branch in the tree.

The two boys went back to gathering nuts.

And the fly returned to its buzzing in the forest. Only this time it picked a tree that wasn't too old to stand up.

Since that day, the mother bird has called the sun every morning. That is why the sun has never been late again.

And since that day, the silly fly has never said another word. All it can say is buzz,

buzz,

buzz.

sing little bird

Sing, little bird,
when the skies are blue;
Sing, for the world
has need of you;
Sing, when the skies
are overcast;
Sing when the rain
is falling fast.

Sing, happy heart,
when the sun is warm;
Sing in the winter's
coldest storm;
Sing little songs,
O heart so true,
Sing for the world
has need of you.

—Maria Hastings

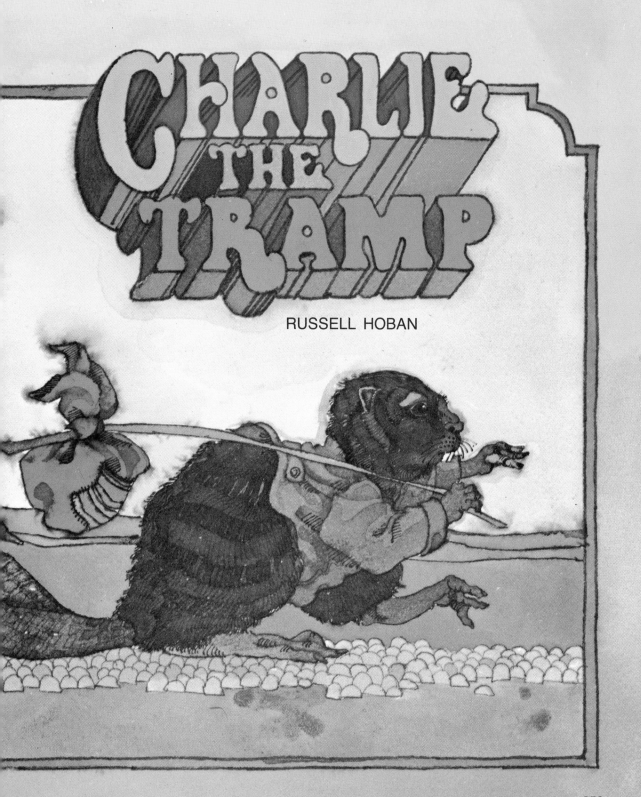

CHARLIE THE TRAMP

RUSSELL HOBAN

"Well, well," said Grandfather Beaver one day when he came to visit. "Charlie is getting to be a big boy."

"Yes, he is," said Father. "He is coming right along."

Grandfather smiled at Charlie and took a quarter out of his vest pocket.

"What are you going to be when you grow up, Charlie?" asked Grandfather.

"I am going to be a tramp," said Charlie.

"A *tramp!*" said Mother.

"A *tramp!*" said Father.

"A *tramp!*" said Grandfather, and he put the quarter back in his vest pocket.

"Yes," said Charlie, "I am going to be a tramp."

"I am surprised to hear that," said Father. "Your grandfather has been doing beaver work for many years, and I, too, am a beaver, but you want to be a tramp."

"That is how it is nowadays," said Grandfather, shaking his head. "When I was young, children did not want to be tramps."

"I don't think Charlie really wants to be a tramp," said Mother.

"Yes, I do," said Charlie. "Tramps don't have to learn how to chop down trees and how to roll logs and how to build dams."

"Tramps don't have to practice swimming and diving and holding their breath under water.

"Nobody looks to see if their teeth are sharp. Nobody looks to see if their fur is oiled.

"Tramps carry sticks with little bundles tied to them. They sleep in a field when the weather is nice, and when it rains, they sleep in a barn.

"Tramps just tramp around and have a good time. And when they want something to eat, they do little jobs for anybody that wants little jobs done."

"I have lots of little jobs for you to do,"
said Father. "You can help me cut saplings for
our winter food. You can help me dig extra
tunnels for our lodge. And, of course, the dam
always needs repairs."

"That is not little jobs," said Charlie. "That's
hard work."

"When I was young," said Grandfather,
"children did hard work. Nowadays all they
want to do is little jobs."

"Well," said Father, "if Charlie wants to be a tramp, then I think he should be a tramp. I think we should not stand in his way."

"The weather is nice and warm now," said Charlie. "May I start sleeping in fields?"

"All right," said Mother.

Charlie tied up some Fig Newtons and some Good & Plenty's in a handkerchief. Then he tied the handkerchief to a stick, and he was ready to go.

"Now it is time for me to be on the road and away," said Charlie.

"Good-by, Mr. Tramp," said Father and Grandfather.

"Good-by, Mr. Tramp," said Mother. "Come home in time for breakfast, and don't forget to brush your teeth tonight."

"Good-by," said Charlie. "Tramps don't brush their teeth."

He got into his little boat, rowed across the pond, and tramped off down the road, while Mother and Father and Grandfather waved to him.

"Now that I think of it," said Grandfather, "I wanted to be a tramp when I was little, just like Charlie."

"So did I," said Father.

"That is how men are," said Mother. "They all want to be tramps."

Charlie tramped down the road, kicking a stone and whistling a tramping song as he went.

He looked at the blue hills far away, and he listened to cowbells tinkling in distant meadows.

Sometimes he stopped to throw stones at telephone poles, and sometimes he sat under a tree and watched the clouds roll by.

Charlie kept tramping until it was almost sundown, and then he picked a field to sleep in. He picked a field where daisies grew and the grass and the clover smelled sweet.

Charlie untied his little bundle and took out some Fig Newtons and some Good & Plenty's, and he ate them while the stars came out.

"Being a tramp is nice," said Charlie to himself, and he went to sleep.

Mother was watching for him at the window the next morning when he rowed across the pond.

"Here comes Charlie," she said to Father, "with his fur every which way and a bundle of daisies on his stick."

"Good morning, Lady," said Charlie when Mother opened the door. And he gave her the daisies. "Do you have a little job I can do for my breakfast?" he said.

"You can bail out the big rowboat," said Father. "That will be a nice little job for you."

"All right," said Charlie. "And then I will eat my breakfast on the back steps, because that is how we tramps do it."

So Charlie bailed out the rowboat. And while he was eating his breakfast on the back steps, Father came and sat down beside him. "How do you like being a tramp?" he said.

"I like it fine," said Charlie. "It is a lot easier than being a beaver."

"How did you sleep last night?" said Father.

"Fine," said Charlie. "But something kept waking me up."

"Was it anything scary?" said Father.

"No," said Charlie, "it was something nice, but I don't know what it was. I will have to listen for it again tonight."

Then Charlie rowed across the pond and went off down the road, whistling his tramping song.

Charlie tramped all day. He listened to the birds singing. He smelled the flowers that grew by the side of the road. Sometimes he stopped to pick blackberries. Sometimes he walked along the top rails of fences.

At lunchtime and dinnertime Charlie went home and did little jobs for his lunch and his dinner.

He stacked winter saplings in the basement for his lunch. And for his dinner he helped his father fix a broken plank in the boat landing.

After dinner Charlie went back to the field where the clover and the daisies grew. Charlie ate his Fig Newtons and his Good & Plenty's, and he listened for the sound he had heard the night before.

Charlie heard the frogs and the crickets singing in the quiet of the night, and he heard something else. He heard a trickling, tickling kind of a little song that had no words.

The trickling, tickling song made Charlie want to hear it better. So he got up and went down to the trees where the sound was coming from.

He saw a little stream that sang as it ran in the moonlight, and he sat down and listened to the song again. But the sound of the trickling kept tickling Charlie, and he could not sit still.

So he took off his clothes, and he dived into the stream and swam around inside the song the water was singing.

Then Charlie climbed out and cut down a little tree that was growing on the bank. When the tree fell down, he rolled it into the water.

Charlie took a deep breath and swam to the
bottom of the stream with the tree and stuck it
in the mud so that it would not float away.

Then he listened to the song of the water,
and he liked it better than he had before. So
Charlie cut down some more trees, and he
began to make a little dam to keep all the
water from trickling away.

Charlie worked on his dam all night. And by morning the stream had widened into a pond. Then the song of the water stopped tickling Charlie, and he said, "Now I guess I can go back to sleep."

So he brushed his teeth to keep them sharp. He oiled his fur to keep it waterproof. And he went to sleep in an old hollow tree by his new pond.

Charlie slept right through breakfast time, and Mother began to worry when she did not see him.

"I am sure Charlie is all right," said Father, "but I think we should look for him anyhow." And he went down to the boat landing and slapped the water with his tail, WHACK!

WHACK! answered Grandfather with his tail, and he came over to see what was the matter.

"I never did think any good would come of letting that boy run off to be a tramp," said Mother.

"That's how it is nowadays," said Grandfather. "Boys run off, and no good comes of it."

So Mother and Father and Grandfather went looking for Charlie, and after a while they came to the new pond. But they did not see Charlie sleeping in the hollow tree.

"I don't remember seeing a pond around here before," said Grandfather.

"Neither do I," said Father. "It must be a new one."

"That's a pretty good pond," said
Grandfather. "I wonder who made it?"

"I don't know," said Father. "You think maybe
Harry Beaver might have done it?"

"No," said Grandfather. "Harry always makes
a sloppy dam, and this one's not sloppy at all."

"What about old Zeb Beaver?" said Father.
"Zeb always makes a good-looking dam."

"No," said Grandfather. "Zeb never makes a
round pond like this one. Zeb always likes a
long-shaped pond."

"You're right," said Father. "He does."

"You know," said Mother to Father, "this pond looks like the ponds you make."

"She's right," said Grandfather. "It does."

"That's funny," said Father. "I didn't make it. I wonder who did?"

"I did," said Charlie, waking up and coming out of the hollow tree. "That's my pond."

"That's your pond?" said Father.

"That's my pond," said Charlie.

"I thought you were a tramp," said Grandfather. "Tramps don't make ponds."

"Well," said Charlie, "sometimes I like to tramp around, and sometimes I like to make ponds."

"Any tramp that can make a pond like that is going to be some beaver one of these days," said Father.

"That's how it is nowadays," said Grandfather. "You never know when a tramp will turn out to be a beaver." And he took the quarter out of his vest pocket and gave it to Charlie.

"Thank you," said Charlie. "Where's Mother?"

But Mother had run back to the boat, rowed across the pond as fast as she could, and had flapjacks and maple syrup ready on the table when the men got home.

The Beaver

The beaver is fat,
and his tail is so flat
that it closely resembles an oar.
He's known for his teeth,
those on top and beneath,
and he lives just a trifle off shore.

He nibbles on trees
as a mouse nibbles cheese
with incisors as sharp as a knife.
And with dexterous tricks
builds a house out of sticks
for his children, himself, and his wife.

—Jack Prelutsky

New Words

The words listed beside the page numbers below are introduced in *The Way of the World*, Level 10 in THE HOLT BASIC READING SYSTEM. Italicized words can be identified independently from previously taught skills.

14. Desta
    father's
    Jima
    stand
    nowhere

16. *hunt*
    monkeys
    Desta's
    arm
    tripped
    sorry
    brighter

17. drum

18. broke
    knife
    dig
    goats

19. spear
    hunters
    spears
    face

20. *joy*

21. *beside*

23. *sunflower*
    garden
    Pipsa
    village
    four
    Pipsa's
    proud
    notice
    fished
    sons
    bags

most

24. *planting*
    year
    seen
    sunflowers
    growing

25. *cakes*
    hair
    start
    herself

26. *reaching*

28. snake
    hoe
    quickly
    keep
    missed

31. *pound*

cake

32. grew
    ideas

33. *Indians*

34. Frederick
    Olmstead

35. *happen*
    itself
    plan
    cities
    hills
    planned
    even
    Frederick's

36. fooling
    Europe

37. *farming*
    kinds
    York
    contest

38. *or*
    trips
    won

39. Central

40. *feed*
    benches

41. *parts*
    plans

44. nice
    Josephine
    Charlie
    Saturday
    meet
    leave

45. *Charlie's*
    hurry
    they'll
    food
    cleaning

46. silly

47. *she'd*
    dolls
    ruined
    he'd
    picnic

48. *picnics*
    sandwiches
    where's
    cousins

50. poles
    acting

wished
worms

51. *snakes*

52. *sure*
    rather
    worm
    ham
    hot
    jam

53. different

54. *hook*
    spend

55. *dumped*
    Josephine's
    hooks

56. *noticed*

57. Max
    who's

58. *kind*

60. Martin
    mayor
    Butch
    Martin's
    Butch's
    happens

61. *remember*
    groceries
    lady's
    election
    campaign
    elected

62. *downtown*
    headquarters
    tables
    newspapers

63. *folding*
    letters
    fold
    meeting

64. *mailed*
    asking
    vote
    air
    fan
    standing

65. flew
    letter
    waiter
    hurrying

68. *elects*
    rally
    please
    hall
    speech

69. microphone
    yelled
    plugged
    wall
    plug
    outlet
    fit

70. *plugs*

71. *leaving*
    within

73. *tries*
    paper

75. job

76. war
    Sam
    Oscar
    stands

78. *means*
    how's
    falls

79. William
    tomorrow

80. promise
    always
    we've

81. acted

82. *mind*

83. waved
    arms
    battlefield

89. *kings*
    each

90. *sometime*

97. Fumio
    dolphins
    sea
    Fumio's
    fishermen
    caught
    many
    swam
    shore
    Taro
    waters
    lighthouse
    fin
    popped
    dolphin

98. threw
    baby
    its

99. worry

100. *sight*
beat
nets
worried
alike

101. *starting*
fins
cut
headed
longer

102. *talks*
teacher
write
hard

103. scientist
scientists
brains
ours
seem
noises

104. *doctors*
seemed

105. sounds
sound
he'll

106. *babies*
teaching
hearing
words
starts
aren't
real
thinks

107. pool

108. *word*
learned

109. *helps*
they'd

110. shell
collection
sand
mornings
beach

111. *calling*
teased

112. *watching*
smiled

113. weeks
bigger
tease
seashells
ear

114. *shells*
spent
afternoons

115. *lovely*

116. while
black
pages
slowly

117. *happily*
museum

118. *led*
cases

119. *wishes*

121. *Ed*

122. Conus
bernardi

127. swallowed
ocean
grandfather
campfire
spirit

128. *upon*
earth
bees

129. *wide*
voice
waves
loud
roll

130. *rolled*
belonged
farther
treetops

131. anger
enough

132. *streams*

133. *treetop*
keeps
mouth

135. *kangaroos*
stood
tails
surely
frog's
eels

136. tied
knot
streaming
clear
lakes
ponds
overcome

138. *remembers*
spirit's
pulls

141. whale
swims
oceans
whales
since
gun

142. born

143. *fed*
milk
warm
hurt
killer

144. *sang*

145. *biggest*
left

149. desert
Abu's
Abu
tent
grass
staying
springs

150. pretend
island

151. *sides*
stars
star
packing
dries

152. oasis
shimmering
drops
deep

153. *greener*
dug
knees
packed

154. *deeper*
seeing
above

155. *tears*

156. *cool*
feels
damp
digging

157. *carry*
dreams

158. bottom

173. *flying*
patchwork
quilt
weren't
collects
stuff
chest
it'll
handy
folded

174. Carl
eye
keeping

175. balloon
wave

176. *promised*
pin
wind
floated
higher

178. *Peters*
jet
lands

179. library
flagpole

180. *hurried*

181. believe

184. *hardly*
kissing

185. *waving*
tear
pinning
grandmother
uncle
ended

188. *dreamed*
wonder
Ellen's
rug

192. race
Pete's
roof
pulled
pigeon
begin
pigeons

193. *Pete*
free

194. *hotter*
ant-like
below
sounded

195. snow
carried

messages
battlefields
late

196. *landed*
badly
noontime

197. *placed*

198. *cared*
lost

199. closer
felt

200. *dot*
carefully
close

205. mystery
Tommy
Sally
Harry
kept
cost

206. *Tommy's*
stories
mysteries

207. *rowed*
Harry's
rowboat
rowboats
anyhow

208. *hope*

209. used

211. *hides*
sunlight
almost

212. *heats*

213. which
north
toward

214. Orion's
belt
Orion

216. *pans*

217. *full*

220. *Walker*
striped
saucer
Alberta
answered

221. *stripes*
pajamas

223. disappear

224. airplanes
airplane
push
pushed
landing

225. loop
loops
dives
field

226. *disappeared*
surprise
dream

227. *others*
believed

228. hurricanes
uncles
aunts
Liz

ate
hurricane
exciting
end
during
hospital

229. fighting
anyway
visit

230. misses

231. storms
winds
fastest
floods

232. girls'
trouble
heading
filling
sandbags
shake
harder

234. somehow
worrying

235. policemen
later
gotten

236. Ramu
kite

237. eight
rupees
kites
bought
fighter
rupee
string

holder
wind
coated
bits
glass
Ramu's
holes
stick

238. held
yards
pushing

239. towards
righted
bit

240. silver

241. charging
battle
sharp
wound
broken
branches

242. float
tall

243. guessed

244. roofs

245. am
awake

246. breeze
buzzing
leaves
crash
buzz
knock
else

247. across

gather
nuts
those
buzzed
mighty
tickling

248. branch
squirrels
scared
elephants
headfirst
nest
six
eggs

249. heart
wake-up
song
wakes

250. ray
fault
wake

251. knocked
gathering

252. seems

254. returned

259. tramp

260. beaver
quarter
vest

262. shaking
young
tramps

263. learn
chop

logs
build
dams
practice
diving
breath
nobody
teeth
oiled
sticks
bundles
weather
rains
barn
jobs
anybody
done

264. saplings
extra
tunnels
lodge
course
dam
repairs

265. fields

266. Fig
Newtons
Plenty's
handkerchief
breakfast
brush

267. tramped

268. kicking
whistling
tramping
listened
cowbells

tinkling
distant
meadows

269. *sundown*
daisies
clover
sweet
untied
bundle

271. *bail*
steps

272. *bailed*

fine
easier
waking

273. *listen*
blackberries
rails
fences

274. *lunchtime*
dinnertime
dinner
stacked
basement

fix
plank

275. crickets
trickling

276. *moonlight*
dived
bank

277. *stuck*

278. widened
brushed
waterproof
hollow

slapped
whack
matter

280. neither

281. pretty
sloppy
Zeb
good-looking
long-shaped

285. flapjacks
maple
syrup